CONTRACTING IN A MANAGED CARE ENVIRONMENT

MARKET-BASED APPROACHES

CONTRACTING IN A MANAGED CARE ENVIRONMENT

MARKET-BASED APPROACHES

ROBERT BONNEY and ROBERT SMITH

HEALTH ADMINISTRATION PRESS
CHICAGO, ILLINOIS

Your board, staff, or clients may also benefit from this book's insight. For more information on quantity discounts, contact the Health Administration Press Marketing Manager at (312) 424-9470.

This publication is intended to provide accurate and authoritative information in regard to the subject matter covered. It is sold, or otherwise provided, with the understanding that the publisher is not engaged in rendering professional services. If professional advice or other expert assistance is required, the services of a competent professional should be sought.

The statements and opinions contained in this book are strictly those of the author(s) and do not represent the official positions of the American College of Healthcare Executives or of the Foundation of the American College of Healthcare Executives.

05 04 03 02 01   5 4 3 2 1

Library of Congress Cataloging-in-Publication Data

Bonney, Robert.
    Contracting in a managed care environment : market-based approaches / by Robert Bonney, Robert Smith.
        p.   cm.
    Includes bibliographical references and index.
    ISBN 1-56793-169-3 (alk. paper)
        1. Managed care plans (Medical care)—United States.   I. Smith, Robert.
II. Title.
        [DNLM: I. Managed Care Programs—history—United States.   2. Health Care Costs—United States.]
    RA413.B664   2001
    362.1'04258'0973—dc21

                                                                                                        2001039754

The paper used in this publication meets the minimum requirements of American National Standard for Information Sciences—Permanence of Paper for Printed Library Materials, ANSI Z39.48–1984. (™)

Project manager: Cami Cacciatore; Acquisitions editor: Marcy McKay; Text design: Matt Avery; Cover design: Betsy Pérez

Health Administration Press
A division of the Foundation
    of the American College
    of Healthcare Executives
1 North Franklin Street, Suite 1700
Chicago, IL 60606-3491
(312) 424-2800

Association of University Programs
    in Health Administration
730 11th Street, NW
4th Floor
Washington, DC 20001
(202) 638-1448

Contents

Preface

"Marley was dead, to begin with."

With the opening words of *A Christmas Carol*, Charles Dickens introduces his central premise to the reader even before any scene, character, action, or theme: the story and its lessons are predicated on the fact of Marley's death. If you miss that point, the author intimates, the rest of the story carries a diminished lesson.

Although less artfully, the title of this book as well as our introductory and first chapters state our premise just as intentionally and unambiguously: managed care is about marketing. The matter of managed care raises the most basic, crucial marketing questions. The answers to these questions require a comprehensive, interactive rethinking of an organization's entire marketing mix—how it perceives its mission, what it considers its core services, how it will deliver those services, how it will price those services (both in terms of level and mechanism), and how it will promote them. Our last chapter, addressing the future of managed care, returns to this premise. In between, we consider serious and significant tactical, operational, financial, actuarial, and even organizational issues surrounding managed care. We examine critical activities such as pricing, negotiating, reporting, and evaluating. First and last, however, we view managed care as a long-term, strategic marketing challenge. Perhaps, unless services are sold on a self-pay basis, it represents *the* marketing challenge.

In our experience, this premise is often at odds with the provider organization's perception in two ways. First, many provider organizations view managed care as a fundamentally financial challenge. Thus, responsibility for managed care contracting often lies with the chief financial officer (CFO). We certainly consider the CFO's involvement critical and would not necessarily argue for or against a leadership role for the CFO. To view managed care contracting as principally a financial function, however, too narrowly interprets its significance and underestimates its strategic, even historic, meaning. Moreover, at least in our experience, CFOs typically demonstrate little tolerance or patience for the ambiguities and complexities of these answers and strike us, at the risk of generalization or worse, as ill suited to lead a discussion of them.

A second way in which this premise of managed care as a marketing issue is at odds with most organizations has to do with how they perceive the long-term, genuinely historic significance of managed care either nationally or locally. Too often, healthcare executives view contracting as an annual activity that simply results in a contract for the next year. We see contracting in the most long-term sense possible, and we ask the reader to do the same for the duration of this book. Minimally, we argue, the reader should look at the implications of this year's contracting in a five-year context. Insofar as managed care contracting has dramatically changed relationships that have been in place for the last seven decades, 10 to 20 years seems to us a reasonable perspective, unless one anticipates a single-payer system in the intervening timeframe.

Derivative from the above premise is this collorary: Because managed care concerns itself with marketing's most basic questions, the provider organization must take a proactive, market-based posture. If managed care involves basic questions—down to and including "What business are we in?"—the healthcare organization could not possibly be too proactive in considering, developing, and acting upon its managed care strategy. Alongside its consumer strategy (becoming more and more critical in this Internet age), an organization's managed care strategy should define the organization's direction for the next decade. And that strategy must by definition be market based. The one-size-fits-all approaches so favored these days by some national payers ignores crucial local considerations and compromises performance.

One final observation: Providers attending the American College of Healthcare Executives (ACHE) program from which we derived this book, "Managed Care Contracting: Pricing, Negotiation, and Management," sometimes perceive that we emphasize the payer's perspective too heavily. Interestingly, payers make the same observation with about the same frequency. For us, if managed care is to work and the relations between payers and providers are to mature rather than deteriorate through managed care contracting, neither and both perspectives are concurrently valid. Thus, while we have published this book through a provider-sponsored organization, we write it in the interest of creating more viable relationships between providers and payers, hope that both can take something from it, and propose that bringing increased value to the member—which should be our constant focus—requires meaningful collaboration.

The lessons of marketing, after all, apply to all of us.

CHAPTER 1

Introduction

"In theory, there is no difference between theory and practice. But, in practice, there is."

—*Jan L. A. Van deSnepsheut*

INTRODUCTION: Managed care means different things to different people. For purposes of this text, managed care encompasses any provider-payer relationship involving a contract—that is, everything except traditional indemnity-type health insurance. This includes traditional preferred provider organizations, health maintenance organizations (HMO), and all of the variations of these organizations that exist in the marketplace for which a provider of health services is paid less than the billed charges.

Many have said that managed care has simply managed reimbursement and benefit design structures, but not the actual care. For managed care to meet its full potential it must move away from the current paradigm and begin managing care. This book is designed to review both managed reimbursement as well as managed care strategies.

CURRENT STATE OF AFFAIRS

More than 81 million Americans (or just over 30%) were enrolled in commercial and Medicare HMOs in 1999. Membership in managed care products represents a significant portion of the insured population in the U.S. (National Center for Health Statistics 2000).

Given the number of people enrolled in managed care plans and their level of satisfaction, it is apparent that some form of managed care is here to stay. It is important for provider groups to understand this and develop a comprehensive managed care strategy. Without such a strategy, an organization will find itself "doing deals" and not getting the desired results. Once the strategy is developed, the organization needs to put in place the necessary structural components to successfully implement the strategy.

POSITIONING THE ORGANIZATION TO DEVELOP A MANAGED CARE STRATEGY

The first step for any hospital, health system, or provider group is to develop a managed care strategy. Prior to developing a strategy the organization must position itself to be successful. The following principles will help an organization focus on the key issues as it develops its strategy.

Competitive Advantage: "You Have to Be Wanted"

Such a strategy needs to first consider the organization's position relative to its competitors. The first rule of managed care contracting is that you have to be wanted. Why should the health plans want to contract with your organization? Many factors influence their decisions and the answer to this question constitutes your organization's competitive advantage.

Attitude Toward Managed Care

An organization's approach toward managed care can provide it with a key advantage. Managed care plans want to work with providers that embrace the concepts of managed care. This does not mean the provider who grudgingly signs a contract, but rather one who is willing to work with the plan to help it achieve its objectives.

The healthcare organization that realizes it is a seller of services and recognizes health plans as the buyer of services will be the successful organization in a managed care environment. The organization that treats the health plan as a customer by both determining and meeting its needs will succeed. This organization will have systems in place to constantly monitor the satisfaction of the health plans with their performance and improve areas in which performance does not meet the plan's standards.

The organization can show its willingness to work with health plans in many ways including:

- Making the organization managed care friendly. This involves an education program for all employees including the importance of managed care to the organization, the goals of the managed care plan, and how the provider organization can help the plan achieve its goals.
- Providing easy access to personnel and documents to the managed care plan's on-site case managers.
- Developing a collaborative relationship between the staff of the provider organization and the plan to manage the care of plan members. This involves working with case managers to move the patients to the least restrictive environment as soon as possible.
- Requiring hospital-based physicians with exclusive contracts to enter into agreements with all of the managed care plans with which the hospital contracts.
- Being supportive of managed care plans' efforts to sign up physicians by providing a forum to address large groups of physicians at a time and encouraging the physicians on the medical staff to sign contracts with the plan.
 - Routinely surveying the health plan to determine its satisfaction with the performance of the organization and implementing corrective action plans when performance does not meet expectations.

Location

Location can provide a significant advantage. For example, if the hospital is the only one located in a major suburb of a city, a plan may need to have the hospital in that suburb in its network to sell its products successfully in the city. It may be willing to pay more for that hospital's services than for the services of other hospitals in its network. As long as all plans are paying the hospital about the same rates for similar volume of services, no one plan is disadvantaged in the market.

Location can also secure higher prices for a health system with multiple hospitals in a city. To the extent that a health system can "corner the market" of one of the key suburbs of a community—but not garner enough market share to raise concerns of antitrust from the Federal Trade Commission—it can gain a significant competitive advantage. With its monopoly-like presence in one segment of the community, the system can leverage that position to get all of its system's hospitals included in health plans. Health plans might be forced to contract with this system or run the risk of significant market share erosion. Again, as long as the health system prices consistently to the health plans, no one plan is disadvantaged in the market and the system can get the rates it wants.

Physician Network

The number, geographic distribution, and quality of the physicians available to the plan from the physician group also influence a system's competitive advantage. Physician groups that cover the entire market area with either a specialty or primary care services and are willing to accept a fixed payment in return for managing and providing healthcare services are the most attractive groups to health plans.

Image

Understand the importance of having a reputation for quality services. Health plans need the key quality providers and hospitals in their networks to be attractive to the market. Do not underestimate the worth of creating and maintaining a strong, positive public image.

Uniqueness of Services

Those hospitals or providers that offer unique services (e.g., lithotripsy, neonatal intensive care unit, burn unit) in the market area have a definite competitive advantage. They must make a strategic decision whether to contract only these unique services to health plans desiring only these services or to only contract with health plans for all the services it offers. The linchpin in making this determination is whether the health plan wants to and can take the patients out of the market area for these unique services.

The health plan that is part of a national company has a unique position. Often these plans provide healthcare coverage to national companies in multiple markets. These national companies tend to be less concerned with the actual providers in the network than with ensuring that there is adequate access for their employees. These health plans have a distinct advantage in that they can direct business to providers to which they would not otherwise have access.

Cost

An organization's cost structure can be a competitive advantage if it permits the organization to price competitively while maintaining a viable position. Thus, organizations should invest in systems that help them control and manage cost.

Being simply the lowest cost provider, however, is not a sustainable competitive advantage because the organization will be viewed as a commodity by the health plan. Once viewed as a commodity, the organization can easily be replaced by other organizations. Thus, while lower cost than the competition is a critical element to an organization's success, it alone may not guarantee successful market positioning.

Quality Outcomes

Outcomes are becoming more important to health plans, but they do not yet drive the decision as to which organization to contract. Health plans want to contract with the health system that can differentiate itself by achieving better outcomes while maintaining a competitive price structure. Health systems and provider organizations must do a better job of making quality and outcomes an issue to the public and employer community if they are ever to drive decision making in the marketplace. Until then, health plans assume that good outcomes are being achieved unless presented with evidence to the contrary.

MANAGING THE COST-PRICE-VALUE RELATIONSHIP

The organization that can successfully manage the cost-price-value relationship will be the one that succeeds in the managed care marketplace.

Hospitals and Health Systems

One of the critical variables that must be known before negotiating managed care contracts is the true cost of services to be provided. Once cost is known, pricing can begin. In order to know what costs are, it is important to have a cost-accounting system in place within the hospital or health system. Such a system will provide management with critical cost information necessary to negotiate prices with the payer.

It is not the purpose of this text to discuss the details of a cost-accounting system, only to assert that one is necessary. Once such a system is in place, it can be used for a variety of tasks, including management of costs and pricing of services.

Management of Costs

For many healthcare organizations the budget is a management tool rather than a planning tool. It is usually the product of a negotiation process between department managers and their vice president, among the vice presidents themselves, etc. Out of this process the budget is born. Then the budget is spread over the year, and the manager is held responsible for meeting it.

The original purpose of a budget is a planning tool, but most healthcare organizations convert it to a management tool. Then when the first month's results are not what the budget projected, the manager must spend time justifying the difference. The savvy manager can easily explain away the differences based on mix of patients, severity of patient illnesses, or other factors. Thus, the cost-control aspect of the budget is negated.

With a cost-accounting system in place, the department manager gets a variable budget each month based on the actual services provided that month. The expected costs given the delivery of those goods and services are also presented. Thus, the department manager gets a report that shows what the costs should be given the mix of services delivered. This is a far better management tool than a negotiated budget.

Pricing of Services

It is obvious that one cannot confidently and accurately price services without first knowing the costs of those services. A good cost-accounting system can provide this information. It can also provide information on fixed and variable costs that can aid in pricing in certain situations (see chapter 2).

The emphasis for hospitals and health systems needs to remain on reducing costs by either reducing utilization or cost per services delivered. These goals can be achieved by continuous quality-improvement initiatives that streamline healthcare delivery processes without negatively affecting the quality of services provided. If future managed care products are designed to account for pricing differences among providers, it will be important to be the low-priced, high-quality provider to be attractive to the managed care plans.

Physicians

Physicians need to know the costs associated with the provision of physician services. Further, they need to know what services they are required to deliver and what services can be appropriately delivered by nurse practitioners and ancillary personnel. By redesigning the delivery processes in their offices, physicians can improve quality and at the same time reduce cost. For example, physicians need to have procedures in place to ensure that their patients are receiving the necessary care. A system to ensure timely preventive services is a must. This not only improves quality, but it reduces cost by preventing future hospitalizations.

The issue for physicians is not their lack of desire to develop the necessary systems to ensure appropriate preventive or clinical services, but rather the lack of time and resources to do so. Here the managed care plan can be helpful. Rather than acting as the "quality police" and telling the physician that he or she is not meeting certain standards, the health plan should act as the communicator of best practices in how to achieve the desired results. In this way, the health plan provides a value-added service to the physician, working with him or her to ensure that an improved service is delivered. Physician-hospital organizations (PHO) should provide this service if health plans do not. In this way, the PHO can provide value to both the health plan and its member providers.

DETERMINING YOUR ORGANIZATION'S ROLE IN THE MANAGED CARE ARENA

Every market is different. Therefore, it is important to determine what position the organization wants to have within its managed care marketplace. The role the organization chooses will affect the structures it must put in place to be successful. Three roles emerge as leading options.

Be a Supplier to Managed Care Plans by Providing Facilities, Physicians, or Both

In this role the organization contracts to provide services to the managed care plan. A critical success factor is the need to "pick your partners well." With all of the consolidation among both hospitals and health plans, it is clear that not all will survive. Thus, it is important for the organization following this strategy to identify who will be the survivors in their market. Long-term survivors include not only the "big-name" health plans, but also local health plans with sufficiently significant market share to compete with the big-name plans.

Once these survivor plans have been identified, the organization should work to develop long-term relationships with them in the form of contracts that are at least five years in duration and cannot be easily terminated by either party. The grounds for termination of these contracts would be specifically detailed in the contract. This type of arrangement gives both parties the incentive to make the relationship work. It provides the health plan with stability in terms of both network and rates and provides the hospital or healthcare organization the assurance of participation in the health plan for the long term.

Where long-term arrangements are in place or where a critical relationship exists, it is recommended that an operations committee be established and meet at least quarterly. The role of this committee is to identify whether the organization is meeting the health plan's needs; to determine jointly how both organizations can be more responsive to meeting the other party's needs; and to discuss any ongoing operational issues as well as future plans being contemplated by either party that could affect the other organization. Members of this group should include the executives of the health plan and provider organization who can make commitments on behalf of their organizations. This ensures ongoing communication at high levels in both organizations and eliminates any surprises that might otherwise strain the relationship.

Be a Payer by Forming Your Own Managed Care Entity
While Continuing to Serve as a Provider to Other Insurers

In this role the organization becomes a competitor with existing health plans. To be successful, this strategy requires the right market conditions and the commitment of time and resources. For example, regarding market conditions, this strategy would be easier to develop if the organization is the sole hospital provider in the market than if the organization is in a market with 15 provider organizations with significant surplus capacity. In the latter case other insurers might choose to terminate their relationships with the organization should it become a competitor. Thus, the strength of its competitive advantage will influence its decision.

The commitment of time and resources is not a small issue. The organization will undergo a significant learning curve. The critical question the organization embarking on this approach must answer is whether the organization has the long-term commitment and sustaining power to undertake such an effort. The structural requirements necessary for success are significant, and a realistic assessment needs to be undertaken before pursuing this strategy (see chapter 6).

Enter into a Joint Venture by Taking a Minority Position in Various Insurance Products

In this role the organization attempts to work with health plans and benefits both as a contractor and an owner of the plan. The organization has more influence than it might if it were not an owner, but less influence than full ownership confers.

Although at first glance this appears to be an easy strategy to implement, it is not. The organization needs to be careful that the health plan it now partially owns does not structure its network, pricing, or benefits so that the high-risk members choose it, causing it to suffer a financial loss, while the lower risk members choose other, more profitable benefit plans offered by the partner insurer. Such adverse selection could end up costing the partner organization significantly if the health plan loses money. Thus, the organization embarking on this strategy would be well-advised to obtain the services of an actuarial consultant at the beginning of the negotiations.

Regardless of the role that is selected for your organization, it is important that the organization address the following critical areas in the development of its strategic plan for managed care:

- *Identify with which plans you want to contract and what type of relationship you want with each plan.* For example, do you want to contract with all plans or only selected ones? Which plans do you want to see grow or develop in your market?

- *Develop a pricing strategy.* As will be discussed in chapter 2, a written pricing strategy is critical to maintaining a strong negotiating position.
- *Develop a product strategy.* For what type of product will an organization contract? For example, will the organization contract for only PPO products when a payer offers both HMO and PPO products or will it only contract for all products or new products? What criteria will be used to make exceptions to your approach? Which types of e-health products meet your objectives?

Certainly variations on these three themes exist. The unique consequences of each will differ depending on the market and the organization's relative strength and competitive advantage. This text will focus on the role of the organization or provider as a supplier to managed care plans. Thus, contracting will be presented as a primary healthcare integration strategy.

REFERENCE

National Center for Health Statistics. 2000. "Table 145. Persons Enrolled in Health Maintenance Organizations (HMO's) by Demographic Divisions and State: United States, Selected Years 1980–99." [On-line source; retrieved 8/28/01]. *www.cdc.gov/nchs/products/pubs/pubd/hus/tables/2000/00hus145.pdf.*

CHAPTER 2

Pricing Considerations

"You got to be careful if you don't know where you are going, because you might not get there."

—*Yogi Berra*

INTRODUCTION: Much has been written about the need for healthcare organizations to organize themselves to take global risk (one fee for all healthcare services necessary for the population covered) by having the infrastructure to manage a fully capitated or percent-of-premium contract. Although many organizations set up the structure to obtain such arrangements, few payers were willing to enter into these types of agreements.

First, inpatient use rates vary depending on the degree of managed care in a market. As long as it is likely that a health plan can reduce inpatient utilization through traditional methods, health plans are reluctant to enter into global risk contracts. This is because the health plan gets the direct dollar-for-dollar benefit of any reduction in utilization, and even if there is only the potential of a 20-day reduction per 1,000 members it is worth it for the plan not to enter into global risk contracts. Once it is unlikely that traditional methods will reduce utilization, then health plans are more willing to consider global risk arrangements; however, by then providers are not interested.

Second, locally owned and operated health plans are more likely to enter global risk arrangements than large multisite health plans. The larger plans need to have flexibility in benefit design options and do not want to renegotiate the global capitation rate each time they enter into a new contract with an employer wanting a different benefit design. In addition, larger plans want to retain control over underwriting, which is often an issue for the local health system because, without this control, adverse selection—for which the provider is at risk—can occur. (See chapter 4 for a discussion of underwriting practices used by health plans.)

Thus, it is important for health systems to understand the various opportunities available through nonglobal risk-pricing methods.

PRICING OPTIONS

A key principle in managed care contracting is to be paid for the risks assumed. This entails knowing the risks and structuring the pricing arrangement to take them into consideration. Each pricing method has its own unique set of risks and rewards.

An organization can be as creative as it wants when establishing pricing options. However, it is important to realize that both the organization and health plan must have the capabilities to administer the arrangement. The best approach is to use a system that allows for automatic processing of claims by the health plan. This autoadjudication process will ensure minimum payment errors. When systems are developed to handle exception-based processing, errors are more likely to emerge. Therefore, it is recommended that the hospital use pricing options that support autoadjudication by the plan.

Pricing methods in managed care contracts follow a hierarchy of increasing risk to the provider accepting payment for services according to different units. The basic theory suggests that the more inclusive the pricing unit in terms of the range of services covered with a single payment, the greater the economic risk assumed by the provider, *other things being equal.* Following this logic, payments to hospitals on the basis of billed charges per unit of service is the least risky pricing unit, whereas percentage-of-premium arrangements would represent the most risky unit of payment from the hospital standpoint. Falling between these extremes, in order of increasing financial risk, are discount, per-diem, per-case, and capitation arrangements. Similar reasoning applies to payments to physicians, but the details of the pricing units will differ between individual and institutional providers.

Do you agree with this hierarchy? The key phrase is "other things being equal." Other things are never equal. Thus, the appropriate answer to the question would be "It depends on a number of factors." For example, if it is likely that the length of stay will decrease over the course of the contract, then a per-diem arrangement may be riskier than a case-rate arrangement. If the health plan controls the utilization and case management, a case-rate contract may be riskier than a per-diem contract. Thus, many factors need to be considered as one assesses the risk of a pricing method.

Selecting the Pricing Option to Use

When responding to proposals it is important to remember that the plan is the buyer and the provider is the seller. Thus, the provider must remember: "If that's the way they want to buy it, then that's the way we have to sell it." If the plan requests per-diem pricing and the provider proposes to use only discounts off of charges, then the provider should not be upset when the health plan rejects the provider's proposal and accepts one from another provider. This does not mean that the provider should not protect against the risks being assumed, but it does mean that there is a need to be responsive to the customer's requests.

For example, a plan requests that the hospital submit a per-diem proposal. The hospital is concerned that the length of stay in the plan will decrease over the term of the contract, thereby reducing the revenue available to cover the hospital's fixed costs. A case-rate or discount-off-of-charge proposal would protect the hospital from this, but it would not meet the needs of the customer. A proposal that addresses the hospital's concern but is also responsive to the health plan should be developed. In this case the objective can be accomplished in any number of ways. One way would be to quote a per-diem rate that covers the variable costs and an admission charge to cover the fixed costs. This would be responsive to the plan's initial request and keep the dialogue open between the hospital and plan.

It is fair to say that providers and hospitals have little choice over the payment methodology that the health plan wants to use. In many cases providers and hospitals will be responsive to the plan's requested methodology. Thus, it is important to be familiar with the available options and the risks and rewards of each.

It is also interesting to note that while health plans want their pricing to be the same for all of their products, they realize that often this is not realistic. The products the health plan offers are different, and thus the level of payment for each should be consistent with the product offered. For example, some health plans offer point-of-service (POS) and HMO products. The HMO products only provide out-of-network benefits in emergency situations. The POS product allows out-of-network access for increased payment. Even though the POS product is technically an HMO product, its benefit design is different and hence the benefits to the provider are different. Pricing for these two products by both the health plan and provider should be consistent with the benefits to the provider.

Determining the Price

As mentioned in chapter 1, it is critical for a hospital or provider as well as the health plan to have a managed care strategy that not only addresses its positioning in the market vis-à-vis managed care but also includes a pricing strategy. Figure 2.1 shows an example of how a health plan might approach a pricing policy.

Whatever the pricing strategy, it is important for the hospital or provider and health plan to price consistently with the strategy. This consistent approach becomes a source of negotiating power (see chapter 5). It will prevent the hospital from giving large pricing concessions to a payer that directs little business to the organization while giving little in the way of price considerations to those who direct a great amount of business. It prevents the health plan from paying outlier rates to non-trauma centers while not paying outlier rates to trauma centers. The organization's pricing strategy will eventually find its way into the market. The question that the organization needs to answer is

Figure 2.1: Sample Health Plan Pricing Policy

Physicians
All physicians will be paid the same fee-for-service rate that represents the 50th percentile of the market. Hospitals whose hospital-based physicians do not sign contracts at the standard rates will have their rates adjusted to offset any premium that is paid to these physicians.

Hospitals
All hospitals will be assessed points for the following factors.
Location
  Market area with no competitors: 10 points
  Market area with one competitor: 5 points
  Market area with two competitors: 2 points
Member Preference
  No. 1 preferred: 5 points
  No. 2 preferred: 3 points
  No. 3 preferred: 2 points
Quality/Image/Outcomes
  No. 1 rated: 5 points
  No. 2 rated: 3 points
  No. 3 rated: 2 points
Primary Care Physician (PCP) Ownership
  > 50 PCPS: 10 points
  40–50 PCPS: 8 points
  30–39 PCPS: 6 points
  20–29 PCPS: 4 points
  10–19 PCPS: 2 points
Managed Care Friendliness
  Extremely friendly: 5 points
  Very friendly: 3 points
  Friendly: 1 point

Recommended maximum price ranges (average per diem) are shown below. Prices below these ranges are desired. In no case will health plan exceed the maximum price for the appropriate range without permission of the CEO.
  30–35 points: $900—$1,000
  20–29 points: $800—$900
  10–19 points: $700—$800
  < 10 points: < $700

whether its pricing policy is defensible when other payers, hospitals, or providers learn of it.

INPATIENT PRICING APPROACHES

Discounts

This method is not very popular with managed care plans. However, it is a popular method desired by network preferred provider organizations (PPO). Many network PPOs get their revenues based on the percentage of savings the PPO brings to the payer. Thus, the higher the discount percentage, the more money the PPO makes.

Often the first managed care entrant into a market is a network PPO. Those hospitals and providers who have maintained a low charge (not cost) structure are often disadvantaged in this situation. It is very difficult for the network PPO to make a profit if the discounts are not significant. They would rather contract at a significant discount with a higher charging hospital or provider than take billed charges from the low charging provider, even if the overall resultant price is higher, because the focus is on the percentage of the discount provided. Thus, those hospitals and providers located in markets not yet affected by managed care would be well advised to raise their prices. It does the provider little good to be the lowest charging hospital or provider in such a situation.

As the market matures and moves away from discounting, being the lowest cost provider or hospital becomes significant. Until then, the emphasis is on charges rather than costs.

Per-diem Pricing

Per-diem pricing is a payment made to a hospital for each day of an admission of a patient. This payment usually is considered payment in full for all services rendered to the member during each day of the admission including, but not limited to, professional fees billed by the hospital, preadmission testing, nursing care, critical care, diagnostic and therapeutic services, ancillary services, durable medical equipment, supplies, medications, ambulance services, and room and board charges, unless specifically excluded in the agreement.

The most common per-diem approach is to pay per diems by category, with the most common categories being medical, surgical, intensive care, step-down, mental health and substance abuse, neonatal intensive care, skilled nursing, and acute rehabilitation. It is strongly recommended that ICD-9-CM and revenue codes be used to clearly define which patient falls into which category to eliminate future disagreements regarding patient classification.

Per-diem pricing is the most common pricing method used by health plans because, in most markets, a significant impact can still be made on hospital utilization. The health plan and their customers get the benefit of this reduced utilization under a per-diem arrangement.

A major risk to hospitals using the per-diem approach is the effect reduced lengths of stay over the term of the contract have on their ability to recover fixed costs. When most per-diem rates are developed, a certain length of stay is assumed. The assumed length of stay is then divided into the total cost for the particular type of stay to arrive at a per diem. Following is an example of the process for developing such a rate.

To develop a medical per diem the hospital would typically determine its average total cost per managed medical patient, in this case $5,000. Next it would determine the average length of stay for these patients, here 5.0 days. This would result in a total cost per day of $1,000. The hospital would want to at least cover its total cost and would therefore charge at least $1,000 per day. Assuming that the hospital was successful in getting $1,200 per day and the health plan was successful in reducing the length of stay to four days, the hospital would receive $4,800 for a stay rather than the $6,000 it had originally expected. Unless the hospital could reduce its cost by $1,200 for medical patient stays, it would be in a worse financial position than expected. If it could not reduce its costs by at least $200 for that last day of stay, the hospital would be in a loss position for this patient type. Thus, reduced length of stay under a per-diem approach is a significant risk to the hospital.

Another risk associated with per-diem arrangements occurs if the health plan has the incentive to hospitalize a patient rather than use the most cost-effective outpatient care. This can occur when outpatient rates exceed the inpatient per diem. The financial incentive would be to admit the patient for a one-day stay at the per-diem rate.

In order to minimize the risk associated with reduced length of stay or admitting patients when outpatient care would be more appropriate (albeit more expensive) two approaches have been accepted by several managed care plans.

Under the admission charge approach the health plan pays the hospital an admission charge for every inpatient admission; this charge is theoretically designed to cover fixed cost and profit. Then a per-diem structure that covers variable cost is established. Thus, as length of stay decreases, the payment lost is that designed to cover variable cost. This is the cost the hospital should be able to save as length of stay decreases.

Under the variable per-diem approach the health plan pays the hospital a higher per-diem rate for the first one or two days. This rate is designed to include the fixed costs associated with a hospital stay. The remaining days are paid at a rate designed to cover the variable costs of the stay.

Another, less accepted approach for dealing with the inappropriate admission concern is to define all one-day stays as outpatient and follow the outpatient portion of the contract. This will not be acceptable to most managed care plans because of the increased administrative burden associated with processing these claims. The more common approach is for the health plan to agree to follow the hospital's utilization review plan for appropriateness of admissions. In cases of disagreement the hospital's utilization review committee would make the final determination.

A new approach has recently been tried in which a hospital has an exclusive arrangement with a payer who has a relatively stable membership. Here the hospital is paid a capitation rate designed to recover its fixed costs and has per-diem rates equal to its variable costs. It is too early to tell whether this approach is having the desired effect;

however, the hospital reporting its development believes it will address their concerns regarding reduced lengths of stay.

The all-inclusive per-diem arrangement is another approach. Here the hospital is paid one rate for all inpatient days regardless of the mix of days. The hospital exposes itself to additional risk using this method because it is now assuming the risk of the mix of patients it receives.

Such a risk may be minimized when the hospital has an exclusive contract with the health plan. Otherwise the hospital assumes the added risk of receiving higher cost patients because of its rate structure. The following case example illustrates one of the risks of the all-inclusive per-diem arrangement.

After several years of having different per diems by category, a hospital entered into a five-year contract with a health plan using an all-inclusive per diem of $780. The hospital offered a full range of services to the health plan and arrived at its rate using historical patient distribution from the health plan:

Service	(a) Utilization %	(b) Current Per Diem	(c)	
Medical	30	850	255	To determine the weighted average all-inclusive rate the utilization % (column a) is multiplied by the current per diem rate (column b) to arrive at column c. Column c is then added up to arrive at the all inclusive per diem
Surgical	40	900	360	
Mental health	15	350	52.50	
Obstetrics	15	750	112.50	
All-inclusive per diem			780	

Shortly after finalizing the contract the health plan was sold to a national managed care company. Upon reviewing the market rates the new management decided that it could buy mental health and substance abuse services from other hospitals for half the rate it was paying to the hospital. The new management then carved out these services to another hospital. Because the hospital was planning on lower-costing mental health patients for 15 percent of its patient mix, it experienced a significant negative effect as the result of this move. (Note that an all-inclusive per diem of $855.80 would now be needed to get the same expected return for the hospital.)

In another case, after entering into an all-inclusive per-diem arrangement with a hospital, a health plan began to send all of its higher-cost cases (e.g., open-heart surgery, transplants) to the hospital. This negative effect was not anticipated by the hospital when it entered into the agreement.

Case-rate Pricing

Case-rate pricing is payment in full for all services provided to the patient during the admission including, but not limited to: professional fees billed by the hospital, preadmission testing, nursing care, critical care, diagnostic and therapeutic services, ancillary services, durable medical equipment, supplies, medications, ambulance services, and room and board charges.

A risk associated with case-rate pricing is that the length of stay may increase or be greater than expected. In such situations the hospital would be well advised to consider the per-diem approach.

The most common case-rate approach is diagnosis-related group (DRG) pricing. When DRGS are used, every admission is assessed through a grouper, which applies the DRG algorithm to assign the final DRG. In long-term contracts the grouper used may become an issue. Because ease of administration requires a hospital to use one grouper, the Medicare grouper is generally favored. This means that contracts negotiated today can be affected either favorably or unfavorably whenever the grouper is changed by the Centers for Medicare and Medicaid Services (CMS). Thus, to be fair to both parties it is important to rebase the rate schedule whenever CMS changes the grouper so that neither party experiences unintended consequences.

Case rates for specific case types—usually including open-heart surgery, angioplasty, heart catheterization, and obstetrics—are also common. Another case-rate approach involves rates for admissions based on categories similar to the per-diem categories. Thus, all medical cases would be paid at one rate, all surgical cases at another, and so forth. Again, it is strongly recommended that ICD-9-CM and revenue codes be used to clearly define which category a patient falls into to eliminate future disagreements regarding patient classification.

All-inclusive case rates expose the hospital to risks similar to those described above for all-inclusive per-diem arrangements.

CONSIDERATIONS APPLYING TO BOTH PER DIEMS AND CASE RATES

A number of factors should be considered when using per-diem or case-rate pricing.

Pricing on the Margin

Pricing on the margin covers an organization's variable costs and a portion of its fixed costs. This technique of pricing should be used in limited situations; otherwise the marginal price will become the base price and an organization will not be able to cover its fixed costs in the long term. Situations in which marginal pricing warrants consideration include the following.

When the Business Being Sought is Truly New Business

For example, when an HMO currently has an exclusive contract with a competitor hospital and the hospital wants the business, marginal pricing may be warranted. In this situation, if the hospital can obtain an exclusive arrangement with the HMO, it would truly receive new volume. If an HMO is contracting with seven hospitals in a ten-hospital market, using marginal pricing may not be the correct strategy unless the organization is certain it will get new business and not just convert existing business to the HMO product.

When the Agreement is Long Term (At Least Five Years)

This criterion is most critical if a hospital decides to use the marginal pricing approach. If the hospital prices on the margin in one-year contracts, competitors who lost business will, in most cases, be eager to recover it. Because the marginal price becomes the maximum price from which the rates are next negotiated, a long-term arrangement is strongly recommended. The contract also should not provide for termination other than for breach, loss of accreditation, or other specifically defined reasons. This forces the parties to work together throughout the term of the contract rather than simply terminating the agreement when there is an issue to be addressed and seeking out other providers.

When the Organization Does Not Have to Add Fixed Costs

If the organization has to add fixed costs to obtain the new business, these new fixed costs must be included in the pricing calculations. Hence, if an organization has surplus capacity that cannot be converted to some other service that will yield as high a return, marginal pricing should be evaluated.

When the Rest of the Market is Pricing on the Margin and the Organization May Have To Do the Same To Retain Market Share

An organization may be forced to use marginal pricing in this situation.

When an organization prices on the margin, it must not forget to consider how the other payers in the market will react. If these payers are significant to the organization, they will demand the same or better rates than the party receiving the marginal pricing. Thus, marginal pricing requires a strategy that addresses the criteria under which the organization will use marginal pricing to avoid the trap of having to price everything on the margin, which would ultimately drive the organization out of business.

Carve Outs

Any exclusions from the per-diem or DRG rates should be clearly delineated (e.g., t-PA [revenue code 259], implants [revenue codes 275 to 278]). The health plan will want to include everything in the rate, whereas the provider will want to carve out high-cost items. With respect to implants, an argument supporting exclusion from the contracted rate is that the health plan selects the physicians with which it contracts; if it chooses physicians who use high-cost implants, it should pay the price. When contracting with a physician–hospital organization (PHO) where the health plan has completely delegated the credentialing function, the PHO is selecting the physicians and it can be argued that implants should be included. Both are legitimate arguments, and a balance must be struck.

Matching Price and Volume

A principle of managed care contracting should be to use price when it means something. Pricing considerations are marketing expenses and should be used when they can direct business to the organization. Thus, the use of incentives to direct business to the hospital should be considered. It is recommended that sliding rate scales tied to volume (e.g., patient days, admissions, total payments received) be developed. The greater the volume, the better the rate. Thus, the health plan has an incentive to direct more volume to the organization than to its competitors.

Table 2.1 illustrates this model. Many health plans do not want to contract using sliding scales because the plans are pricing their product today and therefore want to know their costs today. One way to address this concern is to enter into a long-term contract and fix the first-year rate based on the plan's forecasted volume. The second-year rates are determined based on the actual volume received in the first year. Thus, the hospital is only at risk for not receiving the volume it expected in the first year, and the health plan accomplishes its objective of knowing its prices in advance and not experiencing retroactive adjustments. For example, if the health plan indicates that it will deliver 3,000 patient days for the first year, the pricing will be set using the 2,001 to 4,000 rates. If at the end of the first year the actual number of patient days is determined to be 5,000, the health plan's year-two rates are determined

Table 2.1: Sliding Scale Tied to Volume (Per Diem)

Total Patient Days (All Categories)	Medical/Surgical/ Pediatrics	Intensive Care/ Cardiac Care Unit/Neonatal Intensive Care	Obstetrics
0–2,000	1,000	1,500	1,200
2,001–4,000	975	1,400	1,100
4,001–6,000	950	1,300	1,000
> 6,000	925	1,200	900

using the 4,001 to 6,000 range plus any agreed-to annual price adjustments.

Whenever patient days or patient-day equivalents (which would include a factor for outpatient visits) are involved, it is important that these be clearly defined. For example, are inpatient days counted when they are billed or when the patient is actually in the hospital? This question must be addressed before a situation arises in which one party believes there were 3,900 days and the other 4,100.

Zip code incentives have also been used to encourage use of the hospital. In this case patients who live in zip codes closer to the hospital receive less favorable rates than those who live further from the hospital. The theory is that those patients who live closer to the hospital would use the hospital anyway, whereas the health plan has to give incentives to patients who live further from it. This method also works when a hospital has excess capacity in one but not all services. For example, an urban hospital with excess obstetrics capacity might use the zip code incentive to draw patients from the suburbs.

Annual Price Adjustments

In long-term contracts it is important to address how annual price adjustments will be made. If no adjustments are made during a long-term agreement, the hospital should not expect to "make up" the annual inflation amounts it lost over the term of the contract when the new rates are negotiated. The health plan is not likely to be sympathetic to that argument. Therefore, the hospital should negotiate annual rate adjustments.

The typical approach is to tie the annual increase to either a percentage of the hospital component of the Consumer Price Index (CPI) or Wholesale Price Index. Some contracts tie the rate increase to the volume of business received, as shown in Table 2.2.

Outlier Provisions

To protect the hospital from high-cost cases, outlier provisions are often used. The more typical outlier provisions are:

- When billed charges rendered during a single admission exceed $xx,xxx, the hospital shall be paid a rate of yy% of billed charges.
- The rates due under the contract will in no single case result in payment to the hospital of less than xx% of billed charges.
- When billed charges rendered during a single admission exceed $xx,xxx, the hospital shall be paid a rate of yy% of billed charges; however, the amount the hospital is paid for each day of that admission shall not exceed $zzz. (Note that this amount is usually limited to the ICU rate. The theory is that if a hospital is willing to accept this rate for ICU days, it should be willing to accept it for all days.)

In urban markets with a surplus of hospital beds, it is becoming more typical to find no outlier provisions or provisions only for Level I trauma centers. Outlier provisions, however, are frequently found in rural markets. Outlier provisions can have a significant effect on an overall contract.

For example, assume that a hospital's contract calls for the following outlier provision. When billed charges rendered during a single admission exceed $40,000, the hospital shall be paid a rate of 80

Table 2.2: Sample Annual Rate-adjustment Matrix

Patient Days	Rate-adjustment Factor
0–2,000	Hospital component of the CPI
2,001–4,000	75% hospital component of CPI
4,001–6,000	50% hospital component of CPI + 25% of CPI all items
6,001–8,000	50% hospital component of CPI
> 8,000	Lesser of CPI all items or 25% of the hospital component of the CPI

percent of billed charges. Assume further that the average per diem the hospital receives from the health plan for surgical cases is $1,000. This hospital is a tertiary medical center and has a Level II trauma center. A patient is in the hospital for 30 days, and her billed charges equal $80,000. The plan pays the hospital $64,000, or $34,000 more than the average per diem for similar types of cases. If the health plan had 1,000 patient days in that hospital and no other outliers, which may be unlikely given that number of patient days, it paid 3.4 percent more on the total contract by having an outlier provision; if the health plan had three such patients, it would pay in excess of 10 percent more on the total contract.

Hospitals would be well-advised to retain the outlier provision even if it means compromising on the base rates. The health plan with sufficient clout in the market to eliminate the outlier provision would be well advised to do so even if it has to pay higher base rates.

Utilization and Case Management

The hospital must have utilization and case management systems in place if it is going to price using the case method as the health plan has little incentive to control inpatient utilization once a patient has been admitted to the hospital. The health plan will have these systems in place when it pays using the per-diem method.

RISK-BASED CONTRACTING

Capitation Pricing

Capitation pricing pays the provider organization a fixed fee per member per month to provide agreed-to services. This fee is usually based on the age and sex of the member being covered. For health plans that enter capitation agreements it is important that these agreements be successful for both the plan and the provider organization. Health plans do not want to change their provider networks because doing so is very disruptive to their members. Therefore, most plans will want some degree of oversight of the capitation arrangement to ensure its success. Because chapter 5 is dedicated to the details of risk-based pricing, this section will review only a few key considerations when using capitation as a payment method:

- Use appropriate actuarial support to assist in determining the capitation rates. The actuary can provide advice on anticipated use rates given benefit designs and the population to be covered.
- Ensure that the medical underwriting adjustments are made on a case-by-case basis to the capitation rates—the capitation rates should reflect what the health plan actually receives as premium from its members.
- Align the incentives of all parties (i.e., hospital, physicians, and health plan). A hospital should never take capitation if the physicians receive fee-for-service payment.
- Clearly define the scope of services to be provided and who is responsible for covering each service.
- It is essential that the provider taking capitation have the necessary information and medical management systems in place to manage the arrangement.
- Control additions to or deletions from the network as this could affect utilization in a negative fashion.
- Define the minimum number of covered lives assigned to your risk pool before capitation applies. Generally a minimum of 2,500 to 3,000 lives is needed for a PHO, an IPA, or a specialist, and 250 to 350 are needed for an individual PCP.

The following example provides a case study of a capitation arrangement. In some cases market conditions require providers to accept capitation rates without adequate experience or aligned incentives among the providers. In one such case the health plan required their exclusive hospital to accept capitation while paying the physicians on a fee-for-service basis. The health plan's current utilization was 250 acute days per 1,000 members. In order to protect itself the hospital agreed to a per-member-per-month capitation rate of $25.20. If utilization rates changed so that they were higher than 250 days per 1,000, then the health plan agreed to pay the hospital for each excess day in accordance with the following schedule:

Utilization (d/1,000 Members)	Payment ($/d)
251–259	0
260–268	216
269–276	432
277–285	648
> 285	864

If utilization rates changed so that they were lower than 250 days per 1,000 members, then the hospital agreed to pay the health plan for each lower day in accordance with the following schedule:

Utilization (d/1,000 Members)	Payment ($/d)
249–241	0
240–232	216
231–224	432
223–215	648
< 215	864

By using this approach the hospital was able to limit its risk, provide the capitation rate the health plan desired, and retain the contract.

Percent-of-premium Pricing

Percent-of-premium pricing pays the provider organization a percentage of the premium charged to provide the agreed-to services.

Considerations that are important to the provider organization taking a percent of premium include:

- An agreed-to minimum premium for specific benefit designs.
- Familiarity and comfort with how the health plan handles medical underwriting. This is a critical factor when accepting a percent of premium. The agreement must address medical underwriting procedures and provide for an audit. Failure to adequately address this issue could result in the health plan enrolling high-risk groups at insufficient premiums. The provider organization is at risk for this.
- An understanding of the family size assumptions. Larger-than-expected family size is the risk of the provider organization.

This approach most closely aligns the incentives of the provider and payer organizations, assuming that both the provider organization and payer are truly trying to work together. Percent of premium may be the best payment method for organizations that are owners or partial owners of an HMO.

OUTPATIENT PRICING APPROACHES

Discount off of Charges

Historically, discounting off of charges has been the method used when contracting for outpatient services. This caused hospitals to increase prices rapidly on services that had a significant outpatient component. Many hospitals contracted annually with an accounting firm to analyze their pricing structures and then raised prices significantly on those services that represented considerable outpatient potential. As a result, health plans have moved to more definite pricing arrangements, such as fixed-fee pricing, ambulatory surgical groups (ASC), and ambulatory care groupings (APG), for outpatient services.

More often than not, outpatient fees, regardless of the methodology employed, are being capped at the medical per-diem rate or surgical per-diem rate (for outpatient surgery). Thus, all diagnostic services received in a given day are limited to the appropriate per diem. The theory is that the health plan could admit these patients and receive the per diem; therefore, they should be entitled to limiting payment to the per-diem rate.

Per-visit Fee

A per-visit fee is a flat-rate payment made for all services rendered to a patient during each outpatient encounter. Such payment is considered payment in full, for all services, including—but not limited to—professional fees billed by the facility, nursing care, diagnostic and therapeutic services, durable medical equipment, supplies, medications, facility and ancillary services, and room and board charges if applicable.

Per-visit fees are becoming common for outpatient therapeutic (i.e., observation, physical therapy, speech therapy, radiation therapy, cardiac rehabilitation, chemotherapy, and dialysis); diagnostic (i.e., magnetic resonance imaging, computerized tomography, nuclear medicine, other diagnostic radiology, diagnostic laboratory, ultrasound imaging, and mammography screening); emergency; and urgent-care services. It is recommended that revenue codes be used to clearly define the services that fall within each category.

Many health plans are moving emergency room rates from the per-visit fee to a severity-based system that applies three or four classifications based on the severity of the patient's presenting problems. If such a system is used, the organization should undertake the following.

First, the organization should carefully define the classification system. If possible, the emergency room physician payment system and the facility payment system should parallel each other. It is recommended that the health plan use the prior year's data for emergency room visits to model the payment system. In this way, the plan can determine if there is a trend toward "upcoding" patients as the result of better data capture. Such upcoding will result in higher costs to the health plan. With preimplementation and postimplementation data, modifications to the payment schedule to rebase the rates can easily be accomplished.

Second, the organization should attempt to have the most severe patient classification paid in addition to the inpatient stay. The standard in the industry is to include emergency room charges in the first day of a patient's stay. Thus, unless the patient expires in the emergency room, all the hospital will receive for the most severely ill patient is the agreed-to inpatient rate. Level I trauma centers should carve out trauma cases and these should be paid at a discount off of charges or a negotiated trauma rate.

Outpatient Case Rates

Outpatient case rates are similar to per-visit fees but usually apply to invasive types of procedures (i.e., outpatient surgery and the scopic procedures). These fees are payment in full for all services rendered to the patient including—but not limited to—professional fees billed by the facility, nursing care, diagnostic and therapeutic services, durable medical equipment, supplies, medications, facility and ancillary services, and room and board charges if applicable.

ASC Rates

The most common outpatient case-rate method is ASC rates. These comprise surgical grouping information developed and updated annually by the CMS. When dealing with ambulatory surgery, two key areas should be considered.

First, some health plans modify CMS's ASCs to meet their own needs. It is important that the provider understand any modifications the health plans have made. It is recommended that these become an attachment to the contract to avoid future misunderstandings.

Second, the payment for multiple outpatient surgical or scopic procedures performed during one occasion of surgery needs to be clearly defined. There is no standard industry approach, and each health plan has its own policy on this issue.

APGS are a patient classification system funded by CMS and designed by 3M Healthcare Information Systems to explain the type and amount of resources used during a visit in any ambulatory setting. Patients assigned to a specific APG share similar clinical characteristics and resource patterns. APGS cover only the facility fee for a visit; professional fees are paid separately. A visit can result in one or more APGS. The APG grouper assigns APGS to a visit based on CPT-4 procedure code(s) and ICD-9-CM diagnosis code(s) contained on the UB-92. Thus, it is critical for the facility to have in place systems to capture all appropriate codes and ensure that there is appropriate medical record documentation to support these codes.

The APG system also uses several techniques to combine APGS for payment purposes when multiple APGS occur during a visit:

- Combining multiple related significant procedure APGS into a single APG. This occurs when multiple significant procedures are performed but one requires only a minimal amount of time and resources.
- Including certain ancillary services in the APG weight (i.e., packaging) for a significant procedure or medical APG. High-volume, low-cost ancillary services are typically packaged.
- Reducing the standard payment when multiple nonconsolidated significant procedure APGS or multiple nonpackaged ancillary services are performed.
- Combining multiple encounters for related diagnoses (e.g., preoperative testing with the surgical procedure).

Several health plans are beginning to experiment with APGS. The provider organization needs to thoroughly understand each health plan's model as they may vary.

Ambulatory Payment Classification Rates

The Balanced Budget Act of 1997 required the development of an outpatient prospective payment system for Medicare patients. As a result,

CMS has developed the ambulatory payment classification (APC) system, based on 3M Healthcare Information Systems APGs with modifications. It is likely that many major health plans will follow CMS's lead and use the APC system. Therefore, it is critical for outpatient facilities to become knowledgeable about these changes and how they affect reimbursement.

Fixed Rates by CPT Code or Groupings of CPT Codes

Some payers have been able to get hospitals to agree to a fee schedule for outpatient services based on CPT codes rather than discounts off of charges.

CONCLUSION

Pricing can take many different forms. All methods other than billed charges have some element of risk involved. The critical factor is understanding the risks that are being assumed under the method used.

While creative pricing methods are often used to work toward desired results, it is important to understand what your organization and the payer can administer. Electronic administration is preferred because there is less likelihood for errors to occur. "Keep it simple" is a good rule to follow. Regardless of the method chosen, the organization should invest in an audit function to ensure that it is obtaining the negotiated results.

CHAPTER 3

Evolving Conditions of Belief and Experience

"The history of medicine has been written as an epic of progress, but it is also a tale of social and economic conflict over the emergence of *new hierarchies of power and authority, new markets, and new conditions of belief and experience.*"

—Paul Starr, *The Social Transformation of American Medicine* [italics added]

INTRODUCTION: Successful organizations not only anticipate the future, they compete for it. They do so thoughtfully, aggressively, and, most importantly, with an attitude that they can shape that future. They take the stance that while environmental forces will certainly exert themselves on the organization, the organization itself can influence those forces as well. Just as healthy, successful people face each day with a sense of control and even mastery, so must provider organizations. You may not be able to determine the precise direction of your managed care market, but you should be determined to influence it.

The theme that provider organizations should actively seek to shape an evolving managed care environment underlies this chapter. We argue that both providers and financiers of care can shape the direction of managed care. But only through a cohesive, market-based strategy can your organization compete for its own future. Before going any further, ask yourself: Does our organization have a managed care strategy? Is it written? Disseminated? Understood?

If you do have a written plan, does it:

- Define a managed care strategy as more than pricing objectives?
- Consider where your market has been and where you want to go?
- Identify an action plan to get there?

37

- Differentiate the aims and strategies of the various health plans?
- Anticipate what you will give up in exchange for what you want?

This chapter seeks to articulate why you should develop a managed care strategy and to help you do so based on environmental variables specific to your particular, and peculiar, market. We review considerations about managed care, your market, the various forms of managed care, and the contractual and strategic implications. This chapter looks at the role of market share and the effect of managed care on your market mix. While recognizing the local nature of healthcare, it looks at some universal drivers of change in a way that you can apply to your specific market conditions. This chapter also suggests both short- and long-term objectives of a managed care strategy and provides a step-by-step workbook for devising your own strategy.

PERSPECTIVE: PAST AND FUTURE

Although Starr's observation was not aimed at the emergence of managed care, it could not fit more perfectly with the current situation.

Payers but No Buyers

National health insurance is one of the primary ideologic fields on which the conflict of the shape of healthcare in America has taken place. Such a plan has been brought to the forefront of the nation's consciousness several times. With the Great Depression and the New Deal, conditions might seem to have been propitious for the estab-lishment of a national health insurance. Several movements through the 1930s and 1940s failed to result in a formalized national program, but the privatization of healthcare insurance developed and thrived like a frontier town—pragmatically, unevenly, and, as a national system, by default. Increasingly, first through associations and ultimately through employers, working Americans were "indemnified" against the costs of illness and disease. Then the elderly were similarly indemnified with Medicare. As growing numbers of Americans and billions of dollars in payments poured into the frontier town,

favorable

meddlesome

protected

a healthcare skyline rivaling that of any major city developed on once-empty plains.

Indemnity health insurance did not just provide the economic resources for the construction of the massive American health system (Starr 1982)[1]—by indemnifying or isolating consumers from responsibility for payment, indemnity insurance put control of the demand side of the economic principle of supply and demand almost exclusively in the hands of the suppliers. By allowing providers to simply pass on costs and by ignoring quality, indemnity insurance created little accountability for resource utilization in the hospital and virtually none in the physician's office. Within the so-called system that emerged, buyers and users left quality outcomes and processes to third-party regulatory and accrediting agencies. Quality outcomes were largely defined by the courts, an approach resulting in the medical malpractice crisis of the 1970s. Outside of conformity with guidelines of the Joint Commission on Accreditation of Healthcare or multi-million dollar judgments, each provider or provider organization gave expression to their own definition of quality to the extent to which they were inclined. Patients used the increasingly available resources, and governments and employers paid the bill. Insurers profited to the degree they could properly underwrite and adjust for risk. But no one actually "bought" healthcare in any meaningful sense of the word.

Advent of the Buyer

Since the indemnification of risk for healthcare expense through health insurance in the 1930s, no economic force has changed healthcare more than managed care. Whereas a system of third-party payers seems to have mostly accelerated the growth of the healthcare industry and largely reinforced clinical, technologic, and social trends already taking shape across the landscape of American medicine—first with commercial indemnity insurance and then with governmental indemnity insurance (Medicare)—managed care actually transforms the industry by altering its course and behaviors. By turning to managed care for the solution to rising healthcare costs, employers have leveraged their buying power to create new hierarchies of authority. As group purchasers of healthcare, health plans and payers truly represent new markets for providers.

Such markets should not be entered into cavalierly or stubbornly with old, unexamined notions of what we sell and how we will sell it. Entrants—whether indemnity insurers or providers—must have a short- and long-term strategy based on a thorough understanding of the market's need, the value they bring to that market, and a sense of ability to influence the future. Thus, a managed care contracting strategy must not only answer the question "What do we want from a particular relationship at this time?" but also "What direction is managed care taking in our market? How do we wish to influence that direction? What do we need to achieve that influence?" In other words, "How will we compete for the future?"

New Conditions of Belief and Experience

Consider, in a marketing sense, the monumental impact of indemnity insurance. It effectively bifurcated healthcare into two distinct industries: healthcare financing and healthcare delivery. Over the next several decades each industry developed its own distinct definitions of consumers, pursued its own market objectives, responded to its own unique financial incentives, pursued unrelated strategic directions, created dissimilar infrastructure and information technology, and cultivated consciously unique cultures and conditions of success. These industries related to each other in only the most nominal ways, if at all, and truly operated as separate universes.

Managed care, however, changes all that. Consequently, it requires a change in mindset as dramatic as the difference between the Copernican and Ptolemaic models of the solar system. While managed care assumes decidedly different forms and behaves somewhat differently from market to market, it most basically and inescapably integrates healthcare finance and healthcare delivery into a single industry. No matter how similar some of the functions and characteristics may seem to either insurers or providers, both must recognize that managed care represents a new industry with distinctly new responsibilities and incentives. Moreover, given a different underlying economic reality, managed care also raises new and distinct issues, principles, objectives, and requirements for success.

The key to understanding what creates the new hierarchies of power and control that managed care represents is the fact that integrating delivery and financing creates strong, inexorable incentives to control quality and cost that simply did not exist under indemnity insurance. Unlike an indemnity insurer, a true managed care organization is no mere intermediary whose primary purpose is to "punch and pay" claims. Managed care's mission as an industry is to control costs in the short term. Moreover, mature managed care organizations will, in the long term, recognize that controlling costs means managing quality—an insight from other industries that is not always reflected in health plans' behavior. There is ample reason, beginning at least with the National Demonstration Project for Quality in Healthcare—the initial analysis of whether and how continuous quality improvement would apply in healthcare—and exponentially increasing since, to believe that quality improvement represents the only sustainable strategy.

New Hierarchies of Power and Control

Managed care changes the structure of healthcare delivery in a second, equally profound way: it creates buyers and sellers. The state of medicine today can and should be told as a tale of the interaction, and conflict, between the two. To be sure, the sellers may find fault with the criteria on which the buyers buy, and the buyers may criticize the sellers' ability to demonstrate value, but managed care is about how healthcare services are bought and sold in any given market. For both buyers and sellers, critical strategic decisions will shape their approach to working, or not working, with each other.

In contracting with providers, payers primarily face the question of whether and how closely to work with providers, particularly how they will work with physicians. Many, including some of the largest and most profitable, seem determined to simply leverage their volume purchasing and treat providers as a commodity service. A few go to great lengths to partner with providers, collaborating or even forming joint ventures with them. While in some small part the answer relies on the philosophy of management at the time, providers more accurately anticipate a plan's perspective based on its structure; we will suggest how providers can segment plans by structure later in this chapter. Secondarily, payers will need to decide how selectively they want to work with hospitals and health systems. Will they seek the broadest possible network, increasing access but compromising their leverage, or will they seek to concentrate the purchasing power or partnership with select providers?

To whatever extent they recognize formal or informal differences in provider relations by plans, providers need to begin with the following questions. Do we intend to contract with all plans indiscriminately (or based merely on payment)? Or will we seek to position ourselves to be able to selectively contract with plans over time? If we wish to consider the latter, how do we go about it? However they are predisposed to perceive managed care, providers must answer these critical questions. The answers may rely on the role the provider wishes to play in the marketplace. We suggest defining that role in terms of a market-based response.

A "Pro–Managed Care" Perspective

Before considering a market-based response, however, we will acknowledge what by now you will have discerned: a pro–managed care perspective. We acknowledge this for two reasons. First, if you are not at least open to the possibility that managed care in some form can be made to work to your advantage, then the idea of a managed care strategy (other than resistance and avoidance) may seem either nefarious or marbled with delusion. Second, unless open to this possibility, providers will look to advice from sources such as this book as a means by which to make new rules drive old systems. This approach is directly counter to our intent.

While the vital role that railroads played in the nineteenth-century rise of Chicago as a vast economic and commercial center is well-recognized, it is interesting to note that the very businesses that profited most by their establishment adamantly opposed their construction (Miller 1996). The owners of the city's hospitality infrastructure resisted the railroads out of fear they would eliminate the need for prolonged stays rather than facilitate large volumes of visitors. With parallel irony, despite the fact that private insurance underwrote the economically vast and highly profitable expansion of the medical professions that began during the Great Depression and continues through today, physicians' "distaste for corporate capitalism in medicine was equally [as] strong" as their distaste for socialized medicine (Starr 1982). Physicians were as opposed to "corporate dominance" in the 1930s as they were to government dominance in the 1960s. Yet clearly, albeit retrospectively, both indemnity insurance and Medicare worked to physicians' overwhelming advantage at least as much as did the railroads to the owners of Chicago's hotels, saloons, and brothels.

With these and parallel instances in mind, it is no surprise that the major shift in the conditions of belief and experience represented by managed care continues to meet with such widespread opposition and hostility in healthcare. Moreover, we recognize that much of what some plans do under the banner of managed care represents at best nothing more than managed reimbursement and at worst self-serving financial marauding. Certainly managed care in many markets and by some plans represents some permutation of profiteering, arrogance, myopic or incompetent management, and lack of experience or perspective. Finally, we do not dismiss the legitimate frustration with the inverted social values that bolster without limit payments to entertainers and athletes while ratcheting down the incomes of practitioners who treat human disease and save our loved ones' lives. However, the point is not to complain about the current state of affairs but rather to assess what we can do to advance a more responsible purpose and get about the business of doing so.

True, managed care does change the rules. At best, its financing function no longer underwrites unfettered expansion and marketplace independence and its delivery function intrinsically seeks accountability and requires common definitions and standards. At worst, its proponents may be inexperienced and even ill intended. But this need not bode ill for practitioners willing to meet the same challenge to change that regularly faces providers of goods and services in every other segment of our economy. In fact, managed care should suggest opportunity. In the kind of knowledge-based industry that managed care represents, physicians—healthcare's knowledge workers—should be able to leverage their knowledge into a leadership position. For hospitals and health systems managed care should mean that for the first time in seven or more decades the industry's financial incentives can actually promote, rather than work against, its longstanding and honorable mission.

Managed care will not, however, work to the advantage of either the physician or health system without a coherent, market-based plan of action and a commitment to follow through on it.

WHAT MATTERS IN YOUR MARKET?

With the advent of an actively purchasing buyer and the subsequent requirement that providers behave like sellers, healthcare's market dynamics made the first, incremental movements to fall in line with those of other industries. As it does, we can better use the experience of other industries to project a likely course for healthcare. In particular, we can apply marketing's insights into the interaction between buyer and seller.[2] The more primary of those lessons include:

- Market-driven sellers bring their customers increased value over other sellers.
- While the seller may influence the customer's definition, the customer, not the seller, ultimately defines value.
- Most organizations, and particularly hospitals, have various customers who will likely each define value in their own way.
- Most consumers' sense of value will derive from a variety of end states that must aggregate to an acceptable level.
- Absent the ability to differentiate on other end states, the customer will perceive the service as a mere commodity and default to defining value based simply on price.

The "value chain" conceptualized by Stephen Shortell and others (see Figure 3.1) depicts these lessons quite well. It hierarchically places these "end states" closest to the various stakeholders. But in addition to offering a broader vision of what "marketing" means by demonstrating that stakeholders will assess value in terms they define and measure, it does two other things. First, it graphically demonstrates how marketing success rests on a foundation of management competencies and operational capabilities. Second, it suggests that as stakeholder values change and grow more sophisticated, provider competencies and capabilities will need to evolve as well. We will return to this theme of core competencies both later in this chapter and in detail in chapter 6.

ACKNOWLEDGING LOCAL CONDITIONS

Like politics, all healthcare is local and its transformation—social, economic, technical, or other—unarguably plays out at the local level. Local conditions of market competition refine and nuance adaptive behaviors and forms of the various "species" in a Darwinian way. The presence and growth of nationwide health plans notwithstanding, day-to-day successes rely on a conscious, almost primordial understanding, updated daily, of the local market and its players: their strategies, structures, strengths, and actions. However strong and resourceful they may be, market entrants from other locales who do not quickly read and adjust to local conditions will not be able to leverage their strengths and will over time spend down their resources.

Local Buyers and Sellers

In each marketplace a different configuration of commercial buyers and sellers will interact, each in ways unique to their particular goals, strategies, culture, management, and personalities. Figure 3.2 identifies the key participants that take place in, and are best situated to shape the interaction with, the commercial market. It also provides

Figure 3.1: The Value Chain of Healthcare Delivery

Stakeholders	Communities	Patients	Employers	Purchasers	Gov't	Investors
End States	Ease of Access	Interpersonal Satisfaction	Accurate Diagnosis	Competent Treatment	Positive Outcomes	Affordable Cost	More Knowledge-able Consumer
Competencies	Disease Prevention	Health Promotion	Primary Care	Acute Care Management	Rehabilitative Care Mgt.	Chronic Care Mgt.	Supportive Care
Underlying Capability	Functional Integration		Physician-System Integration		Clinical Integration	

Source: Shortell, S., R. Gillies, and D. Anderson. 1996. *Remaking Health Care in America.* Chicago: Northwestern University (Jossey-Bass Health Series).

Figure 3.2: Profiling Your Marketplace

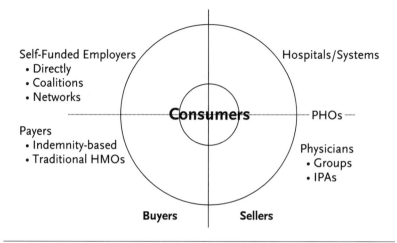

Self-Funded Employers
- Directly
- Coalitions
- Networks

Hospitals/Systems

Consumers

PHOs

Payers
- Indemnity-based
- Traditional HMOs

Physicians
- Groups
- IPAs

Buyers   **Sellers**

a template for profiling the local market in terms of the following players.

Self-Funded Employers

In a system built on employer-funded insurance, the employer market is a logical starting point. Of particular importance is the percentage of employers who self-fund. Basically, these buyers have decided to "make" versus buy the financing component of their managed care approach. Organizations should break down such buyers into those who purchase care

- independently and directly with providers;
- independently but through a network preferred provider organization (PPO);
- as a coalition but directly with providers or a provider network; or
- as a coalition through a PPO network.

Organizations should document the number of employees covered by self-funded employers and consider their opportunities and strategies for directly engaging these purchasers.

Evolving Conditions of Belief and Experience   47

Payers

For reasons discussed below, we differentiate here between indemnity payers and traditional HMOs. Traditional payers may offer PPO, HMO, or hybrid products such as point-of-service (POS) plans. Particularly the HMOs may be for profit or nonprofit, regionally or nationally based, and variously structured (e.g., staff, group, independent provider association [IPA], network).

The Consumer

While we place the consumer in the center of this model, we do not do so based on any belief that the consumer has actually been the focus of attention. All talk of "patient-focused" care aside, indemnity insurance basically disempowered consumers and took them out of play. While many health providers across the country are legitimately and progressively attempting to design consumer-focused models, the real negotiation in the model takes place between nonconsumer buyers and sellers. In a real sense consumers are more in the middle than at the center. Currently it is the providers and either the insurers or in some cases the employer—not the consumer—that shape the landscape of the market.

This, of course, is changing. As we will suggest in chapter 7, technology is beginning to empower the consumer, and economics, in the form of defined contributions by employers, and may very well complete the social transformation of medicine to a consumer-based model. We will discuss such a new model and how it might emerge later. In the interim, however, the model in Figure 3.2 is still useful.

Application of the Model

It should come as no surprise that no two healthcare markets behave the same way if we (1) consider how differently the various players structure and position themselves; (2) recognize important but often unseen or unclear historic personal and professional relationships;

and (3) reflect on how a change in the behavior of one player can prompt changes in the others. Consequently, there is no reason to believe that a specific model that works well in one market will work at all in another. Indeed, it should probably serve only as a reminder that what works well today in that market will probably work less well tomorrow.

Having acknowledged the critical role of local conditions, however, we observe that the same basic principles represent the drivers of change in markets large or small, fragmented or consolidated. However differently the local landscape affects the outcomes of these principles, we can nevertheless apply them to managed care negotiating and contracting strategies. If we understand these principles and focus on what matters in the market, we can influence that market and derive a managed care approach particular to the needs of the community and its stakeholders.

WHAT MATTERS IN MOST MARKETS

Ownership, with which most providers seem obsessed, appears to matter least to consumers. With a few exceptions clustered in the area of public services, consumers demonstrate indifference to the question of who owns what in any segment of the economy. Moreover, we have no experience and know of nothing in the literature to suggest otherwise for healthcare. Consumers do not generally ask who owns the surgi-center or clinic any more than they ask who owns the PPO or HMO; they are indifferent as to whether the organization is for profit, mutual, or nonprofit and whether it is privately held or publicly traded. And, with regard to managed care contracting, consumers particularly do not seem to want to be bothered with understanding what an IPA or PHO is or where the lines with the HMO or PPO begin or end. Although ownership clearly seems to have some effect on HMO behavior, most consumers will not simply want to be bothered. (For an overview of how performance across a number of measures varies by HMO ownership, see the HMO Profile published annually by the American Association of Health Plans.)

What do customers want? Value, although different customer segments—consumers, payers, employers—will define value differently. Consumers want their benefit plan administered properly, and they want access to the care to which that benefit plan entitles them (Herzlinger 1999). They want a sense of value and probably freedom from having to understand the complex system that provides it and the even more complex relationships that influence it. And consumers want control, which typically translates into choice and is increasingly shifting to them through the Internet and the availability of information it provides (see chapter 7). We will come back to the employers and payers who comprise managed care buyers after considering the implications of contracting.

Contracting: Make Versus Buy

If managed care is about how healthcare is bought and sold in the market, then managed care contracting is about make-versus-buy decisions. Buyers contract with providers as an alternative to creating their own delivery systems. Within the last few years even Kaiser Permanente has abandoned a pure make strategy and begun contracting with nonowned hospitals. The same holds true for providers; they contract with managed care plans rather than (or in some cases in addition to) creating their own channels of distribution. In either case the important lesson is that managed care contracting represents a vertical integration strategy. In effect, the plan and provider integrate to provide the full scope of services represented by and provided through a managed care organization.

Given the significance of that relationship, it is important that providers differentiate among the various segments of plans represented by managed care, as the differences will affect not only the terms of the contract but the very future of the provider's market.

SEGMENTING THE MANAGED CARE MARKET

We tend to speak of managed care as if the players represent a homogenous, undifferentiated whole. While the overall aims of the many managed care players may be generally similar, in practice we see widely variant approaches and practices in most markets.

Why Segment?

We suggest the following reasons for applying segmentation to your local market.

Developing a Strategy

As the first step in developing any managed care strategy from the most reactive to the most proactive, providers can actually predict health plan behaviors and to a large degree predicate their own behaviors and strategies on the respective players' strategies and corporate structures. Moreover, identifying the basic corporate structure of a managed care organization, for instance, will tell you whether it is regulated and if so, how.

Analyzing Market Structure

To meaningfully prioritize contracting efforts and pricing decisions you will want to understand who has what market share, how that market share is changing, and who has the edge. You will also want to understand how performance varies by payer in your market. We will look at specific performance measures later.

Determining Win-Win Versus Win-Lose Opportunities

Some plans will present win-win opportunities, and some will not. Either way, it will have less to do with how "nice" or "provider friendly" management is and more to do with corporate structure, regulation, and strategy. Thinking through what you want and what a specific plan can bring based on its structure and strategy can tell you which relationships may develop synergistically and which may not. You might be able to gain more from the most hostile organization than the most friendly.

Analyzing Specific Contracts

The most basic terms of a contract will largely be shaped by the type of organization with which you are dealing. We will discuss this in detail later in this chapter.

Developing Relationships

The very process of gathering the information necessary to profile your market will result in new relationships and sources of information that would not have been otherwise known.

Starting Points

Remember that managed care contracting inherently represents a vertical integration strategy for the provider or provider organization. When you contract with a particular plan or payer, that organization becomes one of your channels of distribution, a function that you are in essence outsourcing. Before making such important decisions you should understand who and what you are dealing with as thoroughly as possible.

While we can most easily distinguish between HMOS and PPOS, we do not recommend this basic distinction as the starting point. We suggest thinking of HMO and PPO as product rather than segment. Look instead at the sponsoring organization and its basic corporate structure. Is it incorporated as an insurer? An HMO? Moreover, once we look at these particular products, it is helpful to make some important distinctions not based on the traditional types (e.g., staff, group, network, or IPA). We propose segmenting the managed care market by the following variables.

Risk Versus Nonrisk Players and Contracts

The most critical differentiation you can make in your market is between the risk holders and the non–risk holders. Why? The complex answer is that non–risk holders serve a different customer, have different aims, employ different strategies than risk holders, and are not regulated in how they do business. The short, pointed answer is that non–risk managed care organizations are significantly limited in what they can offer you in a contract precisely because they do not hold risk. Specifically, they cannot commit to:

- paying you in a timely manner;
- seeing that you get paid at all;
- the utilization standards to which you will be held accountable; or
- sharing any financial incentives.

Basically, network PPOs represent a channel of distribution and nothing more. In fact, certain PPOs may not offer you even that, at least on a "preferred" basis. Only a limited number of network PPOs typically offer your organization any type of steerage in exchange for your discounts. Without advantaging the provider organization with some type of two-tiered benefit plan that gives patients incentives to use it, we find it difficult to understand where the "preferred" in "preferred provider organization" derives from. We recommend at least a 20 percent differential in overall benefits as a threshold for determining a meaningful incentive. Alternatively, if the PPO cannot or will not require a two-tiered benefit plan, then the provider should seek some kind of language limiting the number of competitor organizations with which the PPO contracts.

Insurer Versus Employer

Among risk holders, the difference between insurers and employers is the most obvious and probably the next most significant. Aside from the difference that employers are insuring themselves and insurers are underwriting risk for others, employers are simply small insurers. Yet two other important differences, both of which have significant implications for negotiating contracts, exist: how each is likely to purchase healthcare and how each is regulated.

While either insurers or employers may use network PPOs, larger insurers are likely to establish their own PPO networks, particularly in markets of primary importance. (A common strategy is for an insurer to rent a provider or network PPO in a market that it considers secondary until it aggregates sufficient market share to make maintaining its own network worthwhile.) Unlike network PPOs, insurer-sponsored PPOs can and do offer providers contracted assurances with regard to:

- timely payment;
- tiered benefit structure;
- utilization standards and management programs and standards; and
- financial incentives. (Interestingly, a significant minority of PPOs can and do offer financial incentives, typically in the form of incentive pools.)

As risk holders, employers can make these same commitments. However, given their propensity to use network PPOs—or third-party administrators who in turn either sponsor or subcontract with network PPOs—they often may not. Herein lies one of the key reasons why providers would want to sponsor their own network PPOs capable of contracting directly with employers or their third-party administrators.

While the question of whether the provider organization should sponsor its own health plan—or even contract at risk—is a complex one with an answer that varies from market to market, the question of sponsoring a network PPO is a simple one. Where, as a general rule, providers will want to proceed with extreme caution in the former case, they should assume the need to be particularly aggressive in the latter.

In the presence of a significant self-funded market at the local, regional, or even state level, provider organizations will generally want to sponsor their own network PPOs. While the means of doing so will depend on provider market share, reputation, access to administrative expertise, and other factors, the purpose for doing so is simple and clear: stay close to the customer. Only in relatively rare circumstances will provider organizations want to allow a true third party to intercede in the relationship between the employer/buyer and the provider/seller.

Indemnity HMO Versus Traditional HMO

In our experience the background of a payer makes a significant—if overall qualitative or even subjective—difference, in culture, in perspective, in temperament. The reason seems intuitive enough: traditional indemnity insurers made money in the past principally by risk avoidance. Traditional insurers are strongly actuarially driven and oriented to experience rating. Their business goal may not necessarily have been to get the most business but to get the most profitable business. While they sponsor HMOs, they do so as a product, maintaining risk avoidance and reduction as their core competency. Traditional HMOs, on the other hand, began as a mechanism for risk management rather than avoidance and are more likely to have developed mature medical and disease-management programs. Providers may find that traditional HMOs approach provider and physician relations differently, take more of a partnering approach, and offer more comprehensive and sophisticated demand management and patient education programs.

For Profit Versus Nonprofit

Unlike the difference between health plans with their roots in indemnity insurance and managed care, the difference between for-profit and nonprofit plans has been quantified on several measures of quality of care in at least one significant study. While challenged by both for-profit HMOs and the American Association of Health Plans, in part because of its authors' use of the results to argue for national health insurance, a national study (Himmelstein, Woolhandler, and Wolfe 1999) analyzed 329 HMOs for performance on 14 quality indicators included under the National Committee for Quality Assurance's "Effectiveness of Care" rubric (see Figure 3.3).

The authors point out that for all 14 indicators investor-owned plans had lower rates than nonprofit plans and that "in multivariate

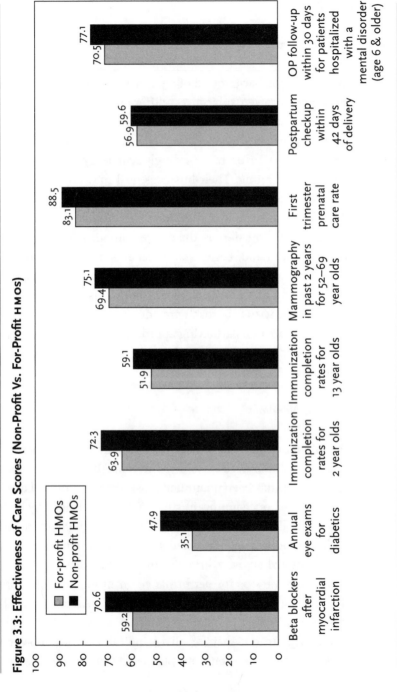

Figure 3.3: Effectiveness of Care Scores (Non-Profit Vs. For-Profit HMOS)

For-profit HMOs
Non-profit HMOs

Beta blockers after myocardial infarction: 70.6 / 59.2
Annual eye exams for diabetics: 47.9 / 35.1
Immunization completion rates for 2 year olds: 72.3 / 63.9
Immunization completion rates for 13 year olds: 59.1 / 51.9
Mammography in past 2 years for 52–69 year olds: 75.1 / 69.4
First trimester prenatal care rate: 88.5 / 83.1
Postpartum checkup within 42 days of delivery: 56.9 / 59.6
OP follow-up within 30 days for patients hospitalized with a mental disorder (age 6 & older): 77.1 / 70.5

analyses, investor ownership was consistently associated with lower quality *after controlling for model type, geographic region, and the method each HMO used to collect data"* [italics added].

We have no doubt in that in any given market some investor-owned HMOs and health plans outperform nonprofits on these or other indicators of quality. How and for whatever reasons these findings are contested, they nevertheless appear to confirm what has long been suspected: Because for profits must satisfy investors and pay higher wages for top executives, nonprofits can spend proportionately higher money on patient care. Moreover, observation of what happens to stock prices of for-profit HMOs when they announce long-term cost-control strategies suggests that nonprofits can more readily partner with providers on approaches that will not yield an immediate return.

We recommend that providers who wish to take a long-term approach in their market and support plans seeking higher levels of effectiveness differentiate among the ownership status of the health plans in their market.

Regional Versus National

While uniformly subject to the same regulatory conditions on a state-by-state basis, a final and often useful point of differentiation between plans lies with the area that the health plan serves. We suggest differentiating between locally or regionally based health plans and nationally based plans.

For local or regional plans, management and operational infrastructure will be housed in the same state and perhaps even the same community as the provider organization. This often makes a difference in how responsive a plan is to both local conditions and local provider organizations. Local or regional plans sometimes accommodate local or regional providers with terms, conditions, and even financial considerations that national health plans never offer. National health plans typically have national contractual, financial, and administrative models that they either do not like to or simply cannot modify. Local executives of multistate health plans typically have no organizational authority over information systems, legal or actuarial services, or other infrastructure within their organization and have difficulty accommodating local needs, however legitimate or sound. Often their responsibilities and compensation incentives are associated simply with sales and profitability, which, particularly if medical management is not locally based, may be seen to derive simply from provider discounts.

Who Has the Edge?

After segmenting your market you will want to consider who has the marketing edge over the other plans in the short and long term. Who will succeed and gain the most in the long term, all other things being equal? Or, as one singularly savvy physician in Savannah, Georgia put it, "Which horse do I ride?"

As we will discuss, HMO growth rates have flattened overall while PPOs continue to grow, largely on the strength of employers' willingness to subsidize choice in a strong economy with low unemployment, but we suggest betting on HMOs in the long run for several reasons. While choice is important and consumers will no doubt continue to require it, the only sustainable advantage in the marketplace is a cost advantage. So who has the cost advantage among health plans? HMOs, clearly and historically (see Table 3.1). We do not expect this to change in terms of either HMOs' inherent price advantage or the importance of that advantage.

We will consider the second point first. If you analyze the composition of your marketplace in terms of employer size, you will likely find that the majority of employees work for firms of 100 or fewer employees. Exceptions of course prove the rule, but most communities are comprised of small employers. Historically, this market is extraordinarily sensitive to price. Price-sensitive employers have typically been willing to change plans for premium differentials of 10 percent or more. Interestingly, HMOs have historically maintained at least an overall 10 percent advantage over PPOs. Moreover, while HMOs are seeing declining enrollment in some markets, they continue to enjoy strong enrollment growth in others.

Table 3.1: Average 2000 Monthly Healthcare Cost by Type of Plan

Type of Plan	Employee Only	Employee Plus Spouse	Family	% Increase from 1999
Indemnity	225	468	632	11
PPO	213	418	569	10
POS	203	417	588	8
HMO	184	375	515	10

Source: "Towers Perrin Health Care Cost Survey." 1999. *Managed Care Week.* January 11. Reprinted with permission of Atlantic Information Services, Inc. Copyright 1999.

While tight labor markets and a strong economy required an emphasis on choice, any softening of the economy will likely result in the HMOs' inherent cost advantage coming to the fore. Moreover, as we more fully discuss in chapter 7, if employees in the future assume responsibility for spending their own dollars—either through flexible spending accounts or a shift from defined benefits to defined contributions—then value-conscious consumers will, acting as prudent buyers, migrate to HMOs.

Can PPOs respond effectively? It is unlikely. Their marketing strength probably cannot stand up to their financial weakness, both of which derive from the same source: open access. The access that consumers prefer—at least when their employer is picking up the majority of the cost—prevents them from tracking and measuring resource utilization rates and trends in any meaningful way. Network PPOs typically cannot even identify with any certainty who is entitled to access their provider panels, and insurer-based PPOs have structural barriers to developing the kind of provider profiling capabilities similar to the more sophisticated HMOs. They can, however, share risk and to that extent are better positioned to align financial incentives.

Which horse should you ride? Clearly most markets outside California at this time are PPO markets. Short-term strategies should play to these purchasing trends. In the long term, however, the wise provider organization will have close relations with the leading HMO(s) in its market, particularly those with successful PPO and POS options, and be prepared to align with that product for the long term.

Performance Measures and Implications

Ultimately, while form or structure may prove useful in predicting performance, providers should monitor and segment health plans in their market based on their actual performance, which will determine any given health plan's future success and tell providers a great deal about who they want to be associated most closely with.

No single variable can predict excellence or success, and no plan will likely be excellent in all regards. Providers should establish a list of criteria that they consider important for profiling plans and then apply those criteria to the major plans in their market. Figure 3.4 provides a list of "Indicators of Excellence" that a provider may use to profile health plans. Externally oriented, these are the very type of indicators of excellence on which consumers are likely to make choices in the future. Figure 3.5 provides a set of performance measures likely to indicate how well a given health plan is performing financially and operationally. Of these more internally oriented performance indicators likely to indicate how well a given health plan is performing financially and operationally, providers may wish to focus on the following three.

Enrollee Change Ratios

One of the most important indicators of current performance and future stability, the enrollee change ratio measures membership retention. Member turnover or change represents a significant administrative and medical cost to health plans. The costs of attracting a new member far exceed those of retaining a current member, and the medical costs are likely to be highest in a member's first year in an HMO, particularly if they are coming from a health plan with less rich benefits. Perhaps better than any other single measure, the enrollee change ratio gives evidence of how good a job enrollees and employers think

Figure 3.4 Indicators of Excellence

1. **Longevity**–with 15 to 20 years experience in your region
2. **NCQA Accreditation**– with plans to use quality measures from the Foundation for Accountability
3. **Non-Profit Status**–with physicians on staff or in a group
4. **Low Angioplasty and Heart By-Pass Rates**–look for 1.6 and 1.5/1000 respectively
5. **Few C-Sections**–15% or less
6. **High Cervical & Breast Cancer Screening Rates**–pap tests for at least 85% for ages 21–64 and mammograms for at least 85% ages 52–64 in last 2 years
7. **High Diabetic Retinal Testing**–at least 64% of the appropriate diabetic population
8. **Follow-up Mental Health Hospitalizations**–96% or more for discharges followed-up
9. **Available Physicians**
10. **High Patient Satisfaction**

Figure 3.5 HMO Industry Performance—Selected Performance Measures

	Reference Points
Enrollee Change Ratio	1.13
IP Days/1000 (All enrollees)	200–250
Physician Encounters PMPM	0.18
Non-Physician/Physician Encounters	0.08–0.10
Days in AR	8.00
Days in Claims Payable	Low 60s
Total Expense as % of Revenue	96–98%
IP Expense as % of Total Medical Expense	27–30%
Medical Expense Loss Ratio	84–88%
Administration Expense as % of Revenue	8–12%
Total Profit Margin	???

the plan is doing and how likely it is to be able to control its expenses in the future.

Days and Encounters

Together with other measures of outpatient utilization, days per thousand and physician utilization will each provide a part of the picture of well a plan can manage medical care. No single indicator, however, is an effective measure. Extraordinarily low inpatient utilization may be an indicator of an efficient plan, or it may simply be accompanied by outpatient utilization that is out of control. Low utilization rates across the continuum of services will likely reflect a plan that has engaged physicians.

Expense Ratios

Providers may wish to monitor various expense ratios of health plans with which it has contracted or is anticipating contracting. Obviously days in accounts payable will indicate the timeliness with which the plan reimburses providers, and total expenses as a percentage of revenue will indicate to a provider both how efficiently a plan is managed and how much it is taking out of the health system for shareholder earnings. In this regard your preference for a high or low medical expense ratio will depend on your perspective. Providers may want to see it as high as possible, nonprofits may want to see it just below a threshold that allows financial stability, and for profits will be generally forced by their stockholders to minimize it in the short term, often even at the expense of long-term benefits.

Value of Segmentation

In the end, the value of differentiating along the variables discussed derives solely from the goals and objectives of the organization's managed care contracting strategy. A provider organization interested only in volume and the short term may choose not to differentiate at all.

On the other hand, an organization seeking to play a more proactive role in contracting, and particularly one concerned with controlling its payment levels over the longer term, will at least differentiate between risk-based and non–risk based plans. Finally, a provider organization interested in influencing managed care's broader, long-term local effect will concern itself with a detailed differentiation of the particular players in its market, advantaging those plans with values and community objectives most consistent with its own.

Where to Obtain Information

Any number of sources for information about health plans exist. Certainly a logical starting point is to simply inventory what you know about a payer from experience. If you have had a contract for years, you no doubt have a good deal of information. However, you may not have the kind of market-based, empiric information you can get from sources such as the following.

Interviews and Relationships

The best starting point is to meet with the health plans in your market regularly. Establish relationships. Ask questions about their priorities and plans. As Steven Covey (1989) puts it, "Seek first to understand." Ask health plans questions such as:

- How are they structured?
- Which geographic and demographic markets do they serve?
- How do they see those markets evolving?
- What are their goals?
- Where would they like to grow?
- How do they approach provider contracting?
- How will their pricing mechanisms evolve?
- How can payment mechanisms be used to align your respective interests and goals?
- How can your organization better meet their needs?

The Departments of Insurance and Health

Although the exact level of detail will vary from state to state, you can obtain a good deal of information from the state within which your service area lies. Insurers and HMOs are regulated by the individual state department of insurance in which they operate, which typically requires annual reporting of specific forms under relatively uniform definitions. Managed care plans organized and licensed as HMOs are also typically regulated by their respective department of health. Both departments may be able to provide meaningful insight into how plans perform.

Employers and Benefits Managers

Employers and benefits managers can provide critical, first-hand insights into the insurer market and its trends. In an employer-funded health system it is critical that the provider organization recognize the primacy of the employer as purchaser and, conversely, that employers understand the value the provider organization brings. Relationships with employers are therefore critical not simply to better understanding, but to being better understood.

Brokers

If you do not know the major insurance brokers in your market on a first-name basis, you should. Meet with them regularly and learn about the market from their perspective. They can give you a good idea of the major health plans' marketing, rating, and pricing strategies, and their level of administrative services and support. They can provide insight into who is gaining or losing in the market.

Private Publications

Various private publications, newsletters, and Internet websites offer pertinent information.

Finally, we recommend that executives of provider organizations seeking to better understand payers join one or more managed care or health plan organizations. Such organizations include, but are by no means limited to:

- American Association of Health Plans;
- American Association of PPOs; and
- state HMO associations.

Educational programs, newsletters, and conferences sponsored by such programs assist healthcare executives in looking at healthcare financing and delivery from a new perspective.

TRENDS AND ISSUES

Having acknowledged that healthcare is a local market and that the interactions between the major buyers and sellers will determine how that local market evolves—and having provided some dimensions along which to measure, differentiate, and even predict the behaviors of some of the key health plans—we turn now to trends in the national marketplace that influence local interactions.

Environmental Considerations

We have already mentioned perhaps the most important environmental consideration: the economy. Aside from the inevitable ups and downs of a market economy is the more immediate fact that healthcare costs seem to be on the rise for a variety of reasons that probably include the graying of America and the aging of the baby boomer. Widely reported in the literature, this trend belies employer perceptions of only a few years ago that healthcare costs had been brought under control. We may now guess that some relatively easy fixes temporarily halted increases and healthcare costs may not be as easily reined in as we thought. HMO premium increases, which historically have sustained themselves below alternative insurance products, have increased for several years in a row.

Although chapter 7 will attempt to peer further into the future and project new directions, considering varied scenarios, the following sections summarize recent and current trends.

Products

As discussed earlier in this chapter, payers were once clearly distinguishable as traditional insurers or HMOs, but both payer types have expanded their product lines, blurring the obvious distinctions. While behavioral differences from underwriting approaches to provider relations still exist, both payer types now offer full product lines that typically include POS options to commercial markets.

Whereas in the mid-1990s both types of plans were aggressively entering alternative markets, particularly Medicare, most plans seem to have concluded that the Health Care Financing Administration's payment levels predestine profitability. In areas where the average area per capita cost is relatively high, principally urban markets, payers continue to offer such products. At this writing, however, healthcare headlines highlight how payers are leaving the Medicare market.

Because network PPOs are not insurers they are not in a position to offer products other than panels of providers and utilization management services to self-funded plans. However, industrial medicine and occupational health for self-funded plans represent a natural market for them. Some of the largest regional network PPOs already offer these services.

Contracting Issues

Contracting trends and issues are being driven by a combination of economics and technology, with somewhat different results depending on the market. We see two dominant trends evolving: fragmentation and incentive payments.

As technology further decentralizes healthcare by allowing more procedures to move to an outpatient setting or the physician's office, those markets dominated by PPOs (principally compensating on a fee-for-service basis) are seeing further fragmentation of the health-care delivery system. Payers who are reliant upon unit pricing to control costs—and yet simultaneously encourage utilization by making volume a source of income for providers—will increasingly carve services out of the relatively more expensive hospital and into the free-standing outpatient center or physician's office. Doing so saves money in two ways: physician-sponsored services are frequently less expensive, and, by offering the physician the opportunity to earn the technical fee, they can further negotiate down the professional fee. Hospitals that began shifting costs in 1983 to the outpatient setting with the introduction of the Prospective Payment System may now be reliant on those margins for their bottom line and be particularly vulnerable to this trend.

Payers contracting in HMO-dominated markets, while exhibiting the same price sensitivity, will tend to look more to the provider organization to control unit cost and delivery system composition. These payers, through partial capitation, global fees, or case rates, are shifting risk for high-volume, low-margin procedures to providers while either sharing or maintaining risk for higher cost services such as inpatient care. With an increased capability over PPOs to monitor performance and profile providers, payers in these markets can and do establish shared incentive plans. Under such contracts, providers who perform better at selected performance measures—from inpatient utilization rates to formulary adherence—are compensated better than those who perform less well. (Chapter 5 will profile such a contract.)

The theme that appears to underlie these trends is economic risk. In markets where payers and providers share little or no risk, contracting appears to be fragmented and less directed. In markets with moderate or high risk sharing, payers tend to contract with provider groups—particularly physician-based organizations—for a market basket of services. In these markets the only commonly carved-out services seem to be mental health and chemical dependency services, for which utilization management requires a different core competency and delivery system than medical and surgical services.

Pricing

Despite pricing increases in insurance premiums of between 6 and 12 percent over each of the most recent years, we know of no markets in which providers are seeing these types of pricing increases. Physician services, now generally related to Medicare's resource-based relative value system (if not expressly derived from it), appear to have dropped over the past several years by as little as 10 percent and as much as 35 percent depending on specialty and market. Hospital inpatient pricing appears relatively flat, again dependent on the market situation, and hospitals can expect to see increased pressure on the outpatient side. In fee-for-service-dominated markets, as noted above, there is no reason to believe these trends will change, other than to possibly accelerate.

As a result, however, it is advantageous for both providers and payers to pursue multiyear contracting, with irrevocable contracts that extend for three to five years and offer both parties more stability than one-year "ever-green" contract terms. (Note that contracts that can be terminated in 90 or 120 days regardless of intended term are not long-term contracts.) Such contracts require providers and payers to work together and give payers the opportunity to offer employers stability over a period longer than just one year. A growing number of contracts feature flexible pricing based on performance, where potential increases in reimbursement are related to achievement of specific outcomes, typically use Health Plan Employer Data and Information Set (HEDIS) measures.

In the last several years yet another trend that promises to continue has emerged: double-digit cost increases (Rollins 2000). Once a relatively insignificant component of the medical expense ratio, pharmaceuticals now represent anywhere from 13 to 18 percent of the premium dollar. In effect, drugs now compete with hospital and physician services as a major healthcare service. Because premium-dollar increases have not kept pace with the doubling of pharmaceutical expenditures from $105 billion in 1999 to $212 billion in 2004 and are not likely to catch up,[3] most health plans project that their drug costs will overtake inpatient services as the largest single component of the medical expense ratio. In effect, through their financial presence and aggressive dissemination of disease-management programs, drug manufacturers and pharmacy benefits managers are competing with physicians and hospitals to reshape healthcare delivery.

Reform

In the absence of any meaningful reform at the national level, state legislatures across the country have zealously taken up the healthcare banner. While any given state may have a number of healthcare reform bills pending, surveys over the past several years consistently reflect a common concern with consumer rights, particularly with regard to access. Numerous states have "any willing provider" laws on the books for PPOS, and several are pushing for open access within HMOS. Interestingly, dozens of states have passed legislation banning so-called "gag" clauses designed to prevent plans from prohibiting providers from talking to patients about their health plan despite the lack of evidence that any insurer or health plan has included such language in a contract.

Executives responsible for managed care contracting should be knowledgeable about state-specific laws affecting managed care and will likely want to subscribe to newsletters or online services that flag and track pending legislation. State HMO associations, as noted, are often a good source of such vehicles.

Industry Performance and Composition

The trend back to premium increases in the early 1990s suggests that at about that time HMOS entered into a period of less robust health. Pressured by alternative products and PPO variants, HMOS saw increased competition combined with rapid increases in pharmaceutical costs and an unfriendly press and legislative environment. Additionally, HMOS had recently entered into new, more problematic markets, having rebounded from the industry-wide weakness of the late 1980s. As a result financial performance suffered despite significant enrollment gains.

As we have seen, however, the managed care industry, and even the HMO sector, is not homogenous and not all plans performed the same. The above financial and commercial pressures created an environment in the last several years that rewards economies of scale, administrative efficiencies, and purchasing power deriving from market share. While some HMOs and health plans lost market share and numerous smaller insurers—or larger insurers not committed to the health insurance market—exited, some HMOs have maintained a margin and continued to grow, reducing administrative expenses and leveraging themselves. Although the short-term challenges of integrating information systems and other infrastructure have humbled even some of the larger, more well known plans in certain markets, the large are getting larger, focusing on penetrating specific target markets and positioning themselves to better drive those markets. We will return to this trend shortly.

Underlying Issues and Challenges

A number of intertwined issues derive from the trend toward healthcare being bought and sold. While we do not mean to intimate that provider organizations can or should be able to predetermine how these issues will play out, they need to understand them in the context of their overall strategic planning and determine how they will deal with the issues in the next several years.

Allocation and Management of Dollars

Managed care contracting is about the allocation of a limited number of premium dollars. As Starr (1982) stated, it is part and parcel of the tale of economic conflict over who makes how much money for doing what. To think, however, that it is about how you price—or, more subtly, what you get paid—is to miss half the point. Managed care contracting is also about what benefit you provide. Competitive markets will reward value, and there is no reason to believe that healthcare should prove an exception to this. However, undifferentiated sectors of industries will not be allocated premium dollars for selling what buyers perceive as commodity goods or services. The conflict over dollars cannot be won by fighting over what you get paid for providing care. You can only gain ground by actually managing care. This, as we will discuss, may change the entire market mix of your organization.

Risk Sharing or Shifting

The opportunity to manage care, however, simply never travels alone. It is inevitably accompanied by the opportunity to manage risk through some type of payment. Under strictly fee-for-service payment arrangements, providers will have little or no opportunity to control their own destiny. As beginning business students are taught every year, "no risk, no reward."

Only a few years ago celebrations seemed to accompany the rise of capitation. Now in many medical communities capitation is being put on trial for all manner of evils, and various providers are calling for its end once and for all. And asking whether those who first hailed capitation are those who now condemn it may miss the point: capitation is only a payment mechanism, and a payment mechanism is nothing more or less than a component of a rational healthcare delivery system. The real issue is not capitation but risk, and the real question of risk has to do with how it is used.

If we accept that managed care is by definition about the integration of the financing and delivery system, then we must accept that risk and reward interrelate. Beyond even this, however, we need to acknowledge that in the end no payment system can occupy a neutral position. The very process of allocating dollars inevitably creates incentives. When the infrastructure of the U.S. health system was underbuilt, an economic model based on cost reimbursement, usual and customary fees, and fee-for-service reimbursement made social and clinical sense. In an economic time of limited resources, excess capacity, and often either uncertain or undocumented benefits, purchasers will require either some form of control or risk sharing.

In the meantime, we arrive at the following conclusions regarding the question of risk (which we will further develop in chapter 4):

- Undifferentiated providers unwilling or unable to negotiate and manage some form and level of risk will find themselves at the lower end of the compensation continuum. They will continue to be discounted heavily as a commodity service.
- Differentiated providers who can demand a higher premium on their services by nature of the marketplace presence and consumer demand will be better paid but unable to otherwise influence the delivery system structure or direction.
- Without some means of sharing risk, physicians and health systems have no effective means of aligning incentives. Fee-for-service-based reimbursement will increasingly put physicians and hospitals in conflicting positions.
- Providers who perceive that some level of quality waste exists in the health system will accept accountability for finding and eliminating that waste and desire to share in the profit that comes from doing so.

The acceptance of risk will not be essential to surviving in the health-care marketplace; it will be essential to influencing its direction. This leads us directly to the next issue.

Network Formulation

Providers concerned only with price for only their specific services may not need to assume risk if they can achieve a differentiated position in the consumer market. Those who do hold the financial risk, however, will continue to make critical decisions about network formation, credentialing of providers, and contracting and recontracting based on their own criteria, needs, and direction. Because the delivery of high-quality healthcare requires a multidisciplinary, comprehensive array of services interconnected and coordinated through some level of common infrastructure, management processes, and measures of ongoing improvement, the matter of network formulation is a critical one.

The mission statement of the provider organization will likely refer to promoting either "the highest quality of care" or "standards of excellence." But in the wake of the National Demonstration Project for Quality in Healthcare and the intervening decade of accomplishment in advancing quality across the country we should now know that this same organization cannot likely achieve its mission alone; quality care cannot exist in a vacuum. We know that the individual hospital is reliant upon others outside its immediate control to achieve that mission and that even the most gifted surgeon can only achieve results in the context of a system in which he or she cannot directly control the entire process. We know that quality outcomes only result from healthcare professionals who recognize their interdependence and commonly commit to establishing and achieving the highest possible standards of care. Knowing these things, it should not surprise us that the establishment of standards represents one of the most fundamental issues of managed care.

Yes, managed care is about who will be paid how much. Certainly it is about whether we should be at risk and for what. Clearly it is also about deciding, or at least having input into, who we work with and refer to. But ultimately managed care must ask a larger question: What are we attempting to achieve and who determines it?

CONTRACTING AS INTEGRATION STRATEGY

Even as, and directly because, managed care represents a vertical integration strategy for both payer and provider, it inevitably and inexorably changes relationships between and among providers—between physicians and physicians, physicians and hospitals, and hospitals and hospitals. In essence, and particularly where providers assume some measure of financial risk, managed care requires providers to relate to each other in new and more collaborative, efficient, value-producing ways.

The central question about integration in healthcare is this: how is value created in health services? Merely having a large asset base, owning a lot of beds, or employing a lot of physicians does not, by itself, create value. What many healthcare executives really seem to be seeking in integration is to maximize the use of their assets, not reduce the per capita cost of care or improve the health of their communities. Contemporary strategies such as physician-hospital organization development or physician practice acquisition are, for many organizations, risky efforts to prop up excess capacity and fixed costs by buying utilization or market share wholesale (Goldsmith 1996).

After years of experimenting with the various forms of horizontal integration the industry has learned (or at least been through) a great deal. Our straw polls, conducted at the beginning of each of the sessions we have taught in managed care over the past ten years, suggest a blend of success, failure, and still-uncertain outcomes. We will not try to summarize the experiences that providers have had as a result of such experimentation, but we will note some conclusions with regard to provider integration in response to managed care contracting.

Integration Continuums

Several years ago a national advisory board published a model suggesting a continuum of organizational integration. We borrow that concept here but point out the critical distinction learned by most providers since then: at least two continuums exist, one for physicians and one for hospitals (see Figure 3.6). Moreover, we will add the following observations.

Hospitals Need Physicians More Than Physicians Need Hospitals

Although this point seems fairly obvious, physicians on nearly any medical staff will probably tell you that it is often forgotten. Moreover, this simple fact, as we will address below, seems to be playing out rather profoundly in key markets across the country. Finally, the same

Figure 3.6: Contracting in Your Market—Integration Continuums

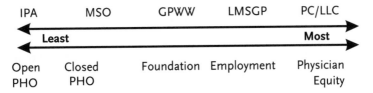

Tier 1: Physician Integration

| IPA | MSO | GPWW | LMSGP | PC/LLC |

Least   Most

| Open PHO | Closed PHO | Foundation | Employment | Physician Equity |

Tier 2: Physician-Hospital Integration

Key to Acronyms:
- GPWW – Group Practice Without Walls
- IPA – Independent Practice Association
- LLC – Limited Liability Company
- LMSGP – Large Medical Single Group Practice
- MSO – Management Services Organization
- PC – Professional Corporation
- PHO – Physician Hospital Organization

can be said in the long term about payers and physicians, although many payers, particularly the national firms, seem not to recognize it.

The Need for Integration Has a Primary and Secondary Driver

The primary driver for determining the required level of integration is economic risk. The greater the risk, as we will discuss in chapter 5, the greater the need for developing a mature infrastructure that can accommodate and succeed under risk by creating value. The secondary driver? Market share, a discussion of which follows. Outside of these two drivers, other motivations will fail.

Complex Environments Require Multiple Models

Most sophisticated players in managed care will recognize that one form does not fit all situations or relationships. Hospitals and health systems will likely involve themselves in various contractual forms depending on need and opportunity.

Physician-Hospital Organizations
Can Work Under Certain Circumstances

Physician-hospital organizations (PHO) have long been forgotten in some communities and continue to serve a vital function in others. We cannot point to one factor to account for the difference, of course. Chapter 7 will discuss characteristics of successful managed care organizations. We will venture a few thoughts here, however, prior to examining what seems to work where. Factors that seem to affect the success of PHOs include:

- the underlying motivation and legitimacy of need for forming the PHO;
- the level of physician input, buy-in, and ongoing commitment;
- the experience and expertise of management in the two critical areas of managed care or insurance and physician relations; and
- the ratio of primary care physicians to specialists.

Whereas the first of the above factors seems rather subjective and intangible, we will suggest a rule of thumb for the last. We have observed—again in straw polls taken during quarterly programs with PHOs across the country—that the closer the ratio of specialists to primary care physicians in a physician organization, the greater its likelihood for success (see Table 3.2). With regard to our poll, we point out that we asked participants to define success in their own terms. The key is not that the PHO meets some specific criteria, but principally that it does what it was set up to do by the participants.

What Works? Where?

Straw polls and individual definitions of success aside, to assess the ability of different integrative forms to succeed under varying market circumstance, we turn to the most recent and comprehensive market

Table 3.2: PHO Physician Composition as a Predictor of Success

Ratio of Specialists to Primary Care	Likelihood of Success
4:1 or more	Extremely unlikely
3:1	Unlikely
2:1	Possible*
1:1	Probable*

*Given the presence of other success factors.

survey we know of: a market-by-market analysis of provider-provider and provider-payer relationships across the country (Coddington, Moore, and Fischer 1996). Figure 3.7 summarizes this original market research that looks at various models and their relative success at obtaining competitive advantage through enhancing value, optimizing primary care services, reducing clinical variation, aligning incentives, and deploying capital. We recommend that the reader review this work personally. Nevertheless, we will point to several important considerations that bear on the theme and conclusions of this chapter:

- *No one structure is "right."* A provider's organizational response to a market depends on the maturity and demands of the market itself. (Once again, form follows function.)
- *Horizontal hospital integration strategies drop off early.* While probably a critical factor in making it to a later stage, without physicians hospital-hospital structures fall off the radar screen relatively early. Hospital-payer structures, despite their ability to capitalize initiatives, do so as well.
- *Physician-physician structures have a longer life.* Provider organizational structures built around physicians seem to take provider organizations further into the future.
- *Both payers and hospitals need physicians.* Physician structures as stand-alone entities do not appear to survive in the most mature markets, but neither do stand-alone hospitals or payers. And while some hospitals enter into the most mature stages of managed care, they do not seem to be the critical partners.

Figure 3.7: What Works Where?

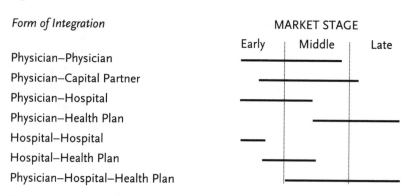

Form of Integration

MARKET STAGE

Early   Middle   Late

Physician–Physician

Physician–Capital Partner

Physician–Hospital

Physician–Health Plan

Hospital–Hospital

Hospital–Health Plan

Physician–Hospital–Health Plan

The right combination of knowledge and capital must come together in a sustainable balance of power.

Competition Through Knowledge-based Partnerships

The future belongs to strategic supplier-distributor alliances in which both parties share a sense of destiny. The study of Coddington, Moore, and Fischer (1996) reinforces that conclusion, as does the experience of other sectors of our economy from package goods retailing to communications and entertainment. Again, we argue that only through strategic alliances can healthcare providers and payers become mature managed care players and that the currency in this transaction is not so much dollars as knowledge.

Visionary suppliers in other industries are creating strategic, knowledge-based partnerships to share business and information with their largest customers. Their intent is to shut out competitors by creating clearly superior customer value through relationships built on a sustainable balance of power (a subtheme to which we will return). That value will be found in every link in the supply chain, right through to what packaged goods marketers call the "first-mover retailer" and managed care calls the primary care physician. Major retailers around the world seem to be moving toward cooperative alliances with a few select suppliers, and we see no reason why healthcare should be any different.

What does that say about the relationships between providers and payers? These relationships will probably exist at any one of several levels and may in select circumstances evolve over time as they interact with and are acted upon by the market. Most will begin as contractual relationships, and in all likelihood only a few will move beyond that. Those that do, however, will be characterized by increasingly aligned incentives and integrated functionality, if not shared infrastructure.

THE ELEMENTAL IMPORTANCE OF MARKET SHARE

From the viewpoint that the decision to enter the managed care market through contracting represents a "buy" decision for either the health plan or the provider, the most elemental matter in defining a long-term strategy deals with defining an overall sense of relationship between a provider and payer. The nature of this relationship will shape the resulting contracting opportunities and the contracts themselves. That relationship must be based on a sustainable balance of power, which derives largely from market share. The relative overall market share of specific payers and health plans determines which of four basic options the participant will need to compete with. Before examining those options, however, we should make one further observation about market share.

Various academics and consultants characterize or stage markets in terms of their maturity. They characterize markets with a high degree of HMO penetration—or markets in which, more precisely, HMOs make much use of capitation—as more mature. While we agree with the general notion that the degree of risk sharing present in any marketplace represents one dimension of maturity, the transference of downstream insurance risk probably serves as a poor proxy for maturity. Rather, we propose to define a mature market as one characterized by:

- The degree to which risk aligns incentives between buyers and suppliers. Simply shifting risk through capitation, for instance, does not necessarily align incentives and may do the opposite, as discussed later.
- A sustainable balance of power between buyers and suppliers, usually measured in terms of market penetration and market share.

We can assess any market in terms of the degree of consolidation and market share of both its providers (either physicians or hospitals) and health plans along a continuum. As the respective industries consolidate, their relationships will be put under increased pressure to change. This means that providers can summarize their strategic situations in one of four categories and even project how their market will likely evolve.

Four Basic Situations and Recommended Strategies

Most readers will agree that the variables that shape healthcare come together in intrinsically different ways in any given locale. Every community, metropolitan area, and region presents a truly unique situation. Whether employers play an active or passive role, the size of the community, personalities of its leaders, composition of its employers, mix of its providers, politics, demographics, and logistics all combine with numerous other considerations to make healthcare a local issue. Recognizing all of that, however, a provider or payer can evaluate the overall situation in terms of four basic situations as a starting point. We will overview each, relating our experiences and recommendations.

Indiscriminate Contracting: Immaturity Personified

In markets in which both provider and payer have many competitors, little market share, excess capacity, and a relatively weak position, both parties will actively and rather indiscriminately contract with each other. While in a sense this type of market allows providers to be very discriminating about which plans they will contract with, in practice they have little incentive to do so. Because of lack of market share few plans can attempt to leverage providers. Health plans in such situations compete on the basis of the number of providers in their panel, and providers typically sign most if not all contracts.

While providers in these markets will feel little inclination to offer discounts or other pricing advantages, we recommend this as the ideal time to consider truly preferential relationships. Few providers may be willing to enter into such arrangements, but they should welcome and even seek contracts with strong steerage incentives that offer significant advantages to the plan as a means of enhancing value. Moreover, providers with both low costs and low charges in such markets should consider increasing their charges, better enabling them to deal with the majority of plans that will insist on discounts.

Health plans in these markets, on the other hand, typically overlook differences in outcomes or cost among providers and single-mindedly seek discounts. Particularly in regard to surplus service providers—hospitals and many specialists—health plans view their suppliers as interchangeable commodities. Ironically, this strategy often leads them to the most expensive facilities with the greatest room for discounting. Such plans should instead take advantage of the immaturity of such markets by planning for the future—identifying low-cost providers with good outcomes and developing sustainable, mutually beneficial relationships. In the longer term such relationships can then sustain more mature activities such as risk sharing and collaboration on measuring and improving outcomes.

Sponsorship: Redefining Our Business

Providers who clearly hold dominant market share in markets where payers are fragmented are well positioned to consider sponsoring managed care products. Providers who lead competitive markets with at least a significant minority (e.g., 35 to 40 percent) or sole-community providers who have at least a significant majority (60 to 70 percent) are considered as having dominant market share.

Providers considering sponsorship will then need to assess the structure of the payer market. In a fragmented payer market it may be better for the provider to offer their own branded and sponsored product, unless a particular health plan offers distinct advantages such as a willingness to collaborate, a wide distribution network, and openness to provider participation in governance. What constitutes fragmented payer markets? A payer with 15 to 20 percent of the market cannot be ignored, and payers with more than 20 percent must be carefully considered. Two requisite conditions exist for considering this strategy. Providers must be able to:

- Provide adequate geographic coverage for the employer market they seek to serve. If single-site employers making health plan purchasing decisions locally dominate the market and the provider can provide adequate access throughout the service area, this condition can be fairly readily met. If the area is dominated by employers who are part of multisite corporations that make their health purchasing decisions centrally and in another market, this condition may be nearly impossible to meet.
- Either redefine their fundamental mission from that of a provider organization to a managed care organization or establish a managed care organization that will have significant latitude to pursue a reengineered delivery system.

Of these two conditions, clearly the second is the most difficult to meet. From large metropolitan medical centers to midsize community hospitals, hospitals across the country have sponsored health plans with widely variant results. In our experience the difference between those that succeed and those that fail more often derives from the fundamental purpose and vision than from deficiencies in management or infrastructure, although the latter requirements must not be underestimated.

Vertical Integration

But what of the circumstance in which both the provider market and the payer market are consolidated? In which a very limited number of health systems and health plans control the majority of their respective market share? These are the markets where contracting will take place on a long-term basis with aligned incentives and recognized mutual interests, markets where strategic purchaser-supplier alliances have been formed and where healthcare is bought and sold based on the value the purchasers derive. This concept of contracting as vertical integration strategy means that in all but the least mature markets, and certainly in the most mature, health plans and provider organizations are beginning to realize what a few have known for some time: they need each other. In fact we would go so far as to state that they are interdependent.

An interesting review of contracting trends in California (Dalzell 1999) points out that after years, even decades, of acrimonious relationships and battling to a standstill, some plans have recognized that they need vibrant, successful physician groups. Rather than driving them to the brink of bankruptcy they are extending them loans and even arranging for consulting expertise when needed. And physician groups are opening themselves up to working synergistically with plans they once mistrusted. In short, plans and physician groups need each other. After all, one sells and provides financing for a service and one provides and clinically manages the majority of that service. This epiphany of mutual dependence has nothing to do with turning over a new leaf. It is based on solid, pragmatic business sense and a recognition that neither alone can provide what matters in the market. Nor does it mean that when negotiations reach an impasse the parties walk away from each other. Rather, when contracting talks hit an irreconcilable snag, they engage a third party to facilitate a resolution.

The results of this approach can be impressive. In the competitive metropolitan Chicago market, the leading health plan has grown its lead to more than twice the market share of its nearest competitor. For years it has taken the approach, at least with regard to physicians—and sometimes hospitals, depending on the posturing and positioning of the hospital itself—that it will only offer an HMO contract to physician groups that demonstrate what Dr. Donald Berwick (1996) called a "context of care," a multispecialty organization capable of providing and facilitating a full continuum of care in accord with written, monitored standards. Over time the plan has moved those performance standards, designed to bring value to patients and employers, in line with its payment mechanisms to reward better performing groups. As plans in California are now beginning to do, it even extended payment advances and loans to physician groups that it recognized as working toward improved performance. The fact that physicians do financially better under this plan and its contracts and consistently rate this insurer higher than its competitors is directly related to the insurer's dominant position.

Specialization

The final possibility lays out a scenario in which a minority of payers controls the majority of a market characterized by fragmented, disparate providers. Many providers may find themselves in this situation now or in the future. Two trends among health plans reinforce the possibility and threat of this scenario.

First, health plans are consolidating and aggregating market share nationally. This occurs on at least two levels. Most obviously, acquisitions—such as Aetna's purchase of Prudential—significantly change the markets in which both plans are already sizable players. However, with little fanfare or press, small and midsized traditional indemnity insurers are also recognizing that managed care represents a new industry with altogether different rules and are exiting the health insurance market. The buyers? Health plans seeking to establish themselves as market leaders.

Second, and perhaps even more significant, managed care organizations use different strategies than their indemnity predecessors. Whereas traditional insurers did not seek significant market share in any given community, preferring instead to simply enroll the most profitable minority of the population through stringent underwriting techniques, managed care health plans are beginning to focus on certain markets. They recognize that to be successful under managed care they need significant market share and exit those markets where they cannot achieve it in favor of those where they can.

In this final quadrant where payers are consolidated and providers are fragmented, providers will be forced through marketplace dynamics and economics into specialization. They find they must become the "focused factory" and do one thing better than anybody else or they will increasingly sell on price. If they can sustain that pricing differential—staking the equivalent market position of a Sam's Club or Wal-Mart—they may survive. Little evidence exists, however, that this approach can work in healthcare.

REDEFINING RELATIONSHIPS AND MARKET MIX

Prior to turning to the question of a defined strategy we will return to the fundamental premise posed earlier in this book—that managed care is about how healthcare is bought and sold and to be a successful seller you have to be wanted in the market. We will look first at the sales side and then the relationship with purchaser.

Market Mix

For many physicians and hospitals being wanted may mean redefining the market mix from the four traditional perspectives of product, place, promotion, and price (see Table 3.3). It will likely mean transitioning from a provider of care to a manager of care, a transition that challenges the infrastructure and culture of most provider organizations. Care managers require sophisticated information and decision support systems, including cost accounting, and active physician support. Care managers will likely have to prove their competency through financial accountability by some form of risk sharing.

Out of almost a sense of self-respect, care managers will not contract indiscriminately. They will actively seek to differentiate among health plans based on how a payer approaches and provides for:

- open flow of reliable information;
- mutual performance targets or accountability;
- opportunity for physician or hospital input; and
- a view of their respective futures as intertwined.

Table 3.3: Re-establishing Market Position

Mix Component	From	To
Product/service	Care provider	Care manager
Place/distribution	Indiscriminate contracting	Selective contracting
Promotion	**Reliance on payer; word of mouth**	Direct consumer; branding
Pricing	Discounted; fixed per unit	Value added; performance dependent

They will selectively contract with those plans that can meet these requirements.

Finally, care managers will take their case directly to consumers, refusing to allow their relationships with their patients to be fully brokered. They will recognize and be adept at not simply public relations or advertising, but consumer marketing, a topic on which we will conclude this chapter.

Win-win Versus Win-lose

We have written a great deal in support of collaborative provider-payer relationships. But can a provider organization form win-win relationships with health plans and vice versa? Yes and no. Clearly it can, depending on the specific market and insurers. Can it do so with everybody? Probably not. Three considerations prevent win-win relations with everybody.

Shear Numbers

Managed care is hard work. The superior customer service and value stored within strategic supplier-provider relationships does not come easy. It requires close collaboration and consistent, ongoing communications. This level of effort will not have a return on investment for many, perhaps even most, of the players in that a given payer may simply not be worth it to a given provider and vice versa.

Structure

As we have seen, many managed care players are not structured for win-win relationships. Network ppos, for instance, may simply not be able to bring the provider the kind of benefit that justifies or allows partnering.

Mindset

The health plan that is not committed to the precept that quality improvement is the only sustainable strategy for cost containment will not be capable of contemplating win-win relationships. Surprisingly and disappointingly some of the country's largest health plans are of such a mindset.

All of this brings us to developing a managed care contracting strategy that makes sense both in terms of local market conditions and the changing times of a transitioning managed care environment.

Exclusivity

One example of what many providers might see as the ultimate win-win arrangement, an exclusive contract, may not necessarily work to the provider's advantage. Remember that contracting represents a make-versus-buy decision to put your organization in play in the health plan marketplace. Once you use a managed care organization as your channel of distribution, you have a vested interest in how many consumers select that plan. Because consumers typically use choice and access as characteristics of quality, tactical expansions to the network, or even of provider organizations that peripherally compete with yours, may benefit you if more consumers select the plan at open enrollment based on the increased access these providers represent. In other words, paradoxically, you may have to share more to get more.

A STRATEGIC MODEL

The transitional nature of managed care certainly warrants an ongoing evaluation of an organization's contracting strategy. Perhaps as often as every six months the contracting organization will want to consider and reconsider its particular strategy and contracts. Nevertheless, any sustainable strategy will be characterized by three basic components and have three somewhat corresponding prerequisites. Within this model we will also suggest pricing and partnering criteria.

Strategic Components

However transitional or stable the market, a contracting strategy for the provider organization will likely embody the following characteristics.

A Tiered Approach

A sensible and durable contracting strategy will differentiate among payers, recognizing that they are, will, or should be more important than others. The value brought by the plan will then be reflected in both financial and nonfinancial terms of the contract. Keep in mind that even in fragmented markets the minority of plans represent the majority of business.

Core Products

The provider organization will reserve at its core its best pricing and promotional efforts. At this core the organization will place:

- any owned or sponsored specialty products such as industrial health or worker's compensation programs;
- any network products for serving self-funded employers; and
- any plans with which the organization may share a financial destiny. This may be in the form or a coequity arrangement or

simply a cosponsorship with a plan from which the organization accepts significant risk. Such a place may be left vacant, however, in the event that a plan does not offer either of these conditions.

Risk and Nonrisk Components

Finally, the plan will differentiate between risk and nonrisk contracts, avoiding downstream insurance risk with plans that cannot bring statistically significant volumes. Health plans that hold risk and are capable of and willing to create financial incentives should gravitate toward the inner tiers, and plans or networks that do not hold risk should gravitate toward the outer tiers because they bring the provider significantly less value and perhaps gain more from the use of the provider's name in their network.

In such a multitiered contracting strategy a provider organization might expect no more than two or three insurers to be so important as to be placed at its core and, if equity is involved, would probably not partner with more than one. In the second tier the organization would likely place the three to seven contracts that account for 75 or 80 percent of its commercial book of business, reserving the third tier predominantly for network PPOs and indemnity payers with nominal market share.

Criteria for Core Partnerships

Effective contracting strategies contemplate both the current contracting or enrollment period and what the provider would like the market to look like in three to five years. We recommend three criteria for tiering managed care contracts in importance for both short- and long-term contracting.

Risk and Reward Participation

Providers who take risk-averse positions must be limited to discounting as a pricing strategy unless they are uniquely positioned in the market. Consequently, we believe the provider organization should first and foremost seek those contracts that reward performance financially. This does not rely on one particular payment mechanism and can be done in any number of ways:

- incentive payments for achieving specific performance targets;
- incentive pools for controlling specific expenses;
- partial or full capitation; or
- current or opportunity equity.

Market share and even current payment levels of the current leaders aside, these criteria represent our number-one recommendation for prioritizing and contracting with a health plan.

Volume and Market Share Potential

Only after profitability should size be considered. In considering which plans will bring your organization the greatest market share and volume now and in the future:

- begin with the obvious—target today's market leaders;
- anticipate tomorrow's leaders as an investor would—after all, putting your organization's name on a product is akin to putting money into it;
- think through a "price:volume ratio" scale; and
- carefully evaluate steerage and panel limitations.

Provider Relations Approach

The final and perhaps most long-term consideration is to rate or rank the health plan's approach to provider relations. Do they emphasize:

- an open flow of reliable information?
- mutual performance targets or accountability?

- the opportunity for physician or hospital input, particularly in regard to clinical matters or policy?
- a view of your respective futures as linked?

In large part this determination comes down to a question of mindset as discussed above.

Pricing

The more successful provider organizations use a written and mutually agreed upon pricing model within their organizations. Such a model establishes common expectations and provides a rationale for proportionate pricing. While exceptions can be made, they may require the agreement of the CFO or CEO.

Typically, a pricing model will employ at least some of the components demonstrated in Figure 3.8. They can take either of two basic approaches. Discount-from-retail pricing represents a growing discount from the organization's published charges based on specific and measurable value that the payer contract brings to the organization. Multiple-of-wholesale pricing represents an add-on to an organization's minimum acceptable price.

As inferred above in considering market share, the range of pricing will usually reflect the degree of consolidation or fragmentation in the market. In the absence of any strong health plans with deep market share, a pricing strategy can be relatively compact and shallow. The opposite, however, can very well apply. In either case, once the provider decides on appropriate range variables that are used to tier, price can include:

- gain sharing or risk sharing—the willingness of the payer to provide a performance-based payment bonus;
- volume—the shear number of lives or market share that the payer brings to the table; and
- steerage—the willingness to limit the number of providers participating in the plan up to and including the possibility of an exclusive arrangement.

Figure 3.8: Establishing a Tiered Pricing Strategy

	DISCOUNT from RETAIL		
	Peripheral	Secondary	Primary
Gain Sharing	0	0	10
Volume		10	15
Steerage		10	15
Total Up To	10%	20%	40%

	MULTIPLE of WHOLESALE		
	Peripheral	Secondary	Primary
Gain Sharing	10	10	
Volume	15	15	
Steerage	15	0	
Total Up To	140%	125%	100%

In order to keep it relatively simple, more than three variables would not be used. In fact, total volume and steerage might more appropriately be reduced into a single variable such as actual volume or admissions once experience has been gained with the plan.

CONSUMER MARKETING: THE ULTIMATE LEVERAGE

Before concluding this chapter we would like to point out that as important as we consider the relationship between providers and payers, we consider it secondary to the provider's relationships with consumers. After all, to further their own purpose of enrollment growth, payers will only feel compelled to contract with providers whom employers insist be included in the contracted panel, and employers will only insist on providers they and their employees prefer. As we said at the beginning of this book, to sustain a successful managed care contracting strategy you must be wanted in the marketplace.

Therefore, patient satisfaction and clinical outcomes important to consumers represent the ultimate managed care strategy. From this perspective, critical components of your strategy are no more or less simple than:

- a smooth and efficient registration and admitting process by staff who are both consumer friendly and adequately trained (to capture and record the required insurer mnemonics);
- patient care staff who recognize that they are in the patient information and service business as well as the patient care business;
- a team approach to meeting consumer needs among people with a common vision who are trained in continuous quality improvement and empowered to act on the results of process improvement; and
- patient bills that are as clear and easily understood as a credit card statement.

In other words, you must run a market-driven organization that recognizes the patient as consumer. In the final analysis consumer preference in your local market represents your ultimate managed care leverage.

CONCLUSION

Managed care dramatically poses the most fundamental marketing question: How will healthcare be bought and sold? In addition to requiring an understanding of who the buyers are and what they seek, it raises and requires different answers than market-mix questions of the past such as:

- How do we define the services we sell? Are we selling the pro-vision of healthcare services or the management of healthcare services?

- How will we distribute our services? Through our own managed care products, as a subcontractor, or both?
- Will we compete on price or does the opportunity exist to differentiate ourselves? If we seek to differentiate, how can we do so in such a way as to be adequately compensated?
- How will we promote ourselves and our services? To consumers? To employers? To health plans?

By definition managed-care contracting represents a vertical integration strategy for both plan and provider. In executing the contract providers literally become part of the health plan with which they contract and should be prepared to proactively support its success in the market. Consequently, as suppliers, contracting providers should carefully segment and evaluate their managed care markets and its players based on their own strategic plans and long-term objectives. Based on an analysis of the compatibility of the health plan's direction and its current position, providers should develop and continually evaluate a tiered contracting strategy.

In addition to the most elemental marketing question, managed care contracting raises two additional, basic strategic questions: the financial question of how funds will be delivered and the clinical and operational question of how healthcare will be delivered. We will address the first of these questions in chapter 4 as part of our consideration of fund and risk allocation and the second in chapter 6 on building the infrastructure necessary for mature managed care organizations.

NOTES

1. Appropriately subtitled "The Rise of a Sovereign Profession and the Making of a Vast Industry," Paul Starr's book *The Social Transformation of American Medicine* provides an excellent history of the development of what he terms "private" (and we refer to as "indemnity") insurance. Anyone concerned with influencing the direction of managed care will find this book as relevant today as when it was written.

2. Even today, however, at least two decades after the marketing function was first introduced into the hospital setting, marketing continues to be

mistaken or used as a proxy for advertising, public relations, or sales. We use marketing in the much more inclusive sense of scope of services and the delivery, pricing, and overall promotion of those services.

3. This projection resulted from a study conducted by the School of Pharmacy at the University of Maryland projecting that drug costs will increase by 15 percent to 18 percent per year over a five-year period. The study indicated that about 60 percent of that increase derives from "near-equal prices and utilization increases in drugs that are already on the market" (Rollins 2000).

REFERENCES

American Association of Health Plans. 1999. *1999 Industry Profile: A Health Plan Reference Book.* Washington, DC: AAHP.

Berwick, D. 1996. "Quality of Care. Part 5: Payment by Capitation and the Quality of Care." *New England Journal of Medicine* 335 (16): 1227–31.

Coddington, D., K. Moore, and E. Fischer. 1996. *Making Integrated Health Care Work.* Englewood, CO: Center for Ambulatory Health Care Administration.

Covey, S. R. 1989. *The 7 Habits of Highly Effective People: Powerful Lessons in Personal Change.* New York: Simon & Schuster.

Dalzell, M. D. 1999. "HMOs, Physicians Discover They Really Need Each Other." *Managed Care* 8 (11): 39–42.

Goldsmith, J. C. 1994. "The Illusive Logic of Integration." *Healthcare Forum Journal* 37(5): 26–31.

Hamel, G. and C. K. Prahalad. 1994. *Competing for the Future.* Boston: Harvard Business School.

Herzlinger, R. 1997. *Market Driven Healthcare.* Reading, MA: Addison-Wesley Publishing Company.

Himmelstein, D., S. Woolhandler, and S. Wolfe. 1999. "Quality of Care in Investor-owned vs. Not-for-profit HMOs." *Journal of the American Medical Association* 282 (2): 159–62.

Miller, D. 1996. *City of the Century: The Epic of Chicago and the Making of America.* New York: Simon & Schuster.

Rollins, G. 2000. "Double-digit Drug Cost Increases Predicted for the Next Five Years." *Managed Care Outlook* 13 (17): 5.

Starr, P. 1982. *The Social Transformation of American Medicine: The Rise of a Sovereign Profession and the Making of a Vast Industry.* New York: Basic Books.

ADDENDUM A

CASE STUDY: HEALTH PLAN SPONSORSHIP BY
A COMMUNITY HOSPITAL

A few years ago when HMOs were coming out of a period of significant financial losses overall, a large community hospital determined to sponsor its own "insurance strategy." With revenues of more than $250 million, a strong bottom line, and approximately 32 percent of the market (in a town with nine other hospitals), the hospital dominated the market in this community of approximately 300,000 people. After teaming up with the next-largest facility, a 300-bed tertiary facility with another 25 percent of the market, the joint venture was funded with just over $9 million and the HMO was launched—the eighth of eight HMOs serving a highly unionized town.

Early Problems

As if starting a new plan in a town with eight other HMOs and nearly 40 percent HMO penetration were not challenge enough, early problems nearly doomed the initiative. Some of the barriers included:

- a multimillion dollar lawsuit by the largest insurer alleging anticompetitive behavior;
- a boycott on the part of the primary care physicians;
- daily distrust between the administrative and medical staffs of the two hospitals;
- delays in achieving state approval;
- inflexibility on the part of the management company that had been retained; and
- mounting development costs.

With the recruitment of a new CEO, termination of the management agreement, and reorganization of an executive team committed to both engaging physicians and providing customer service, the HMO began to turn around.

Key Management Decisions

Fully supportive of the new management team, the board agreed to re-structure key committees for optimizing physician input. Revamped information systems allowed revised physician compensation methods with accountability and feedback. Physicians began enrolling, and objections from the state department of insurance regarding access were overcome. Sales focused on side-by-side offerings at larger employers with a history of offering HMOs and on their employees who had a history of using them. Early enrollees, for whom a well-trained patient services department (accountable to the vice president for marketing, whose incentives now included membership retention as well as new sales) had rolled out the red carpet, reinforced through word of mouth an aggressive advertising campaign using all available local media. Enrollments began to outpace those of competitors, and the plan grew significantly. By the third year, largely under pressure from its hospital owner to expand its targeted markets, the plan rolled out a small-group (under 25 employees) product and growth accelerated.

Unbudgeted Losses Mount

Through the first two years losses accrued, but at levels consistent with the revamped budget. In year three, just at the time the plan's financial forecast projected that it would begin generating a profit, losses per member per month increased. Instead of a slight profit the plan experienced a slight loss. That loss aggregated to $2.5 million in year four.

"Why?"

The board, owner hospitals, participating physicians, and management all had, of course, the same question: Why? In turn, each of the following was examined and several things seemed clear.

- Revenues, adjusted for membership, were at or above budgeted levels for one of the two hospitals that had promised to commit its employees. The fact that the other hospital never included its employees was a source of both conflict and distraction.

- Administrative costs, while slightly above the long-term budget in absolute dollars, were actually below budget on a per-member-per-month basis.
- Medical expenses, varying widely from product to product, overall demonstrated a loss ratio of nearly 90 percent, well in excess of the budgeted 84 percent. Although inpatient utilization in days per 1,000 was below the targeted levels, outpatient utilization clearly was running higher than expected in certain specialties.

Different Perspectives, Different Solutions

An analysis of this plan's medical costs from a range of profiles points out how different interpretations of what constitutes the problem will result in different answers about what to do.

In profiling medical expense by product the plan discovered that the majority of its losses (approximately $1.5 of $2.5 million) could be attributed to the minority of its members in the small-group product. The hospital's conclusion was that management had entered into the small-group market without proper underwriting criteria, incurring unnecessary loses. It needed to tighten underwriting criteria (already consistent with its competitors) and sanction the brokers who had brought those particular contracts to the HMO. Management's conclusion was that the small-group business is inherently risky and turbulent, with wide variations in profitability. According to management the plan had prematurely entered the small-group business at the insistence of the hospital owner and used competitive underwriting criteria.

In profiling medical expense by primary care physicians the plan demonstrated that 80 percent of the budget variance could be attributed to 5 of the approximately 55 physicians who had at least 200 patients enrolled with them. These 5 physicians had annual member costs of at least two standard deviations from the mean of the remaining 50 physicians. Had these physicians' economic profiles mirrored the average of their peers, the health plan's costs would have been reduced by $2 million. The hospital's conclusion was that these five physicians represented some of the most active admitters of Medicare patients, and any kind of sanctioning would risk the loss of business for the hospital and its facilities. Management's conclusion was that the five physicians were not providing optimal care and should be financially sanctioned and given a period to reduce utilization, after which they should be dropped from the panel if they continued to demonstrate utilization practices outside the norm.

In profiling medical expense by service type the plan's experience for the previous 12 months indicated an overall favorable experience for physician costs. Primary care physician expenses were within 3 percent of budget, and specialist costs per unit of service were at the budgeted level. Moreover, total physician costs were running approximately 10 percent below those of the plan's largest competitor, providing the plan with an overall advantage. Hospital inpatient costs per diem, however, were 30 percent above the filed cost reports for the plan's nearest competitor, and outpatient costs for specific services at the hospital were from 60 percent to 200 percent of what the plan would have been able to contract for those services outside of the hospital network. Management demonstrated that if its inpatient expenses were comparable with those of its competitors, the plan would have saved nearly $2.7 million, giving it a modest bottom line for the year. Management sought both reduced per diems and the ability to add less-expensive outlying hospitals, arguing that such additions would both reduce base inpatient costs and foster enrollment growth. The hospital took issue with management's financial and utilization management, indicating that the plan needed to improve its competitive position by reducing specialist utilization. The CFO argued that plan volume did not warrant additional discounts and that adding outlying hospitals would further erode the plan's ability to steer patients to the owner hospital.

Outcome

The initial concern on the part of the hospital—that competing health plans would no longer contract with the sponsoring hospital—never materialized. The hospital continued to contract with all the major area plans while under the original management team its own startup plan grew to become the second-largest HMO in the area within four years.

Increasingly, however, the differences in perspective brought plan and hospital management into conflict. By the end of the fourth year tensions and conflicts over the plan's strategies and operations rose to such a degree that the plan CEO resigned and was replaced by the hospital's finance director, who reported to the hospital CFO, and within a year all but one of the plan's senior executives were gone. Within the subsequent 12 months the hospital reduced its per diems to the plan, added three additional outlying hospitals, and implemented a financial compensation plan for physicians based on their profiles. Within two years the hospital CFO was asked to resign by a new health system CEO. Today the plan is the largest in the area, and it has generated a positive bottom line for the past four years.

Conclusions

Under specific circumstances hospitals and health plans can and possibly should sponsor their own health plans. These conditions are likely to include:

- significant market share and geographic coverage;
- the ability to provide the majority of health services and specialties;
- competent management evaluated on their results in running the health plan;
- adequate financial resources;
- the absence of a single dominant insurer that could "punish" the hospital by moving a large volume of business; and
- a willingness to operate the health plan as a discrete business.

Probably no single managed care strategy or activity can bring into sharper focus the need for new conditions of belief and experience than health plan sponsorship.

CHAPTER 4

Reasonably Allocating Funds and Risk

"Money is a terrible master, but an excellent servant."

—*P. T. Barnum*

INTRODUCTION: Having considered an overall contracting strategy and the multiple payment mechanisms that can be used within a contracting strategy, we will now examine various aspects of resource allocation and payment mechanisms in some detail with the intent of providing a context for determining the reasonableness of payments for contracts you negotiate. As such, chapter 4 will:

- provide definitions and sources of risk as well as the methods of underwriting or rating risk;
- provide a starting point for benchmarking typical costs by service type for both commercial and Medicare populations;
- consider implications of the distribution of insurance risk on utilization and utilization management; and
- explain and consider capitation as both a payment mechanism and a convenient proxy for evaluating the allocation of healthcare costs.

A few words on this latter point. While just a few years ago national advisory groups heralded capitation as some type of financial savior, more recently many seem willing to nail it to a cross of criticism. While either position can be rationalized, perhaps neither can be fully justified.

Capitation, as we will discuss, can clearly and demonstrably work under the right set of circumstances and within the appropriate context. It continues to serve select organizations across the country quite satisfactorily. Various provider groups anticipate its expansion. On the other hand, true and troubling stories of financial frustration and failure involving capitation abound. In either situation capitation is merely a technical tool. Its success in terms of reducing unwarranted utilization and even bolstering provider incomes certainly speaks to its potential. That said, we can only conclude that where it has failed, such failure speaks more about the practitioner than the tool. Finally, in both success and failure, an examination of capitation provides powerful lessons for examining one of the most critical issues in healthcare—the flow of funds and the rational distribution of limited resources.

Therefore, while we will seek to examine capitation's role (if any) in the context of a rationally structured contractual relationship between payers and providers, we will use it simply to examine the interdependence of unit use and unit cost in dissecting and understanding total component costs. Even if you never anticipate or desire a capitated contract, an understanding of capitation assists with better negotiating of any type of risk-based contract. The ultimate approach to "flexible budgeting," capitation's measurement—dollars per member per month (PMPM)—serves very well in examining this issue of the allocation of healthcare costs and resources.

WHY RISK-BASED CONTRACTING?

We begin with the preliminary question "Why even consider risk-based contracting?" Although we will defer until later in the chapter the companion question of whether risk contracting can be accomplished fairly to both providers and payers, it seems reasonable to address this fundamental question up front. After all, should providers accept financial responsibility for genetic or behavioral risk factors over which they have absolutely no control? One could reasonably argue that:

- alcohol abuse and poor driving habits increase health plan costs by approximately 10 percent;
- smokers cost health plans an average of 30 percent more than nonsmokers; and
- members with significant weight problems increase costs by 37 percent.

Beyond member behavior we can ask, "Should providers be financially affected for the vagaries of insurance risk or the aggressiveness of underwriting practices?" Costs for predictably high-utilization organizations may easily run 35 percent or more above the community norm and 50 percent or more above the lowest utilizing risk pools. Providers accepting risk, even where that risk is adjusted by such traditional factors as age and sex, may well be at risk for unintentionally inexact, purposefully predatory underwriting practices. And finally, could we not argue that shifting risk to the provider obviates the role of the health plan itself? If insurers do not insure, what exactly is their role? Simply sales?

Two Different Questions

To some extent and in many places the question of whether providers should accept risk is moot. Other than pure, old-fashioned cost-plus reimbursement (both product and symbol of an altogether different era in American medicine), any payment mechanism represents some type of risk—marketing or financial, business or insurance. Consider the following conditions of belief for risk-based contracting.

1. *Opportunity for Financial Gain.* If you believe quality waste exists in the delivery system and that you can reduce it, you will be willing to assume the risk to accrue the reward.
2. *Alignment of Incentives Among Providers.* If you believe hospitals and physicians need to work together to improve quality and control their own destinies, you will seek to avoid the fragmenting incentives for self-interest of fee-for-service (FFS) payment.

3. *Autonomy.* If you want to influence who participates in your local delivery system and how clinical decisions are made, you will be willing to spend your own money through a fixed payment mechanism. (If you want to spend someone else's money, you will allow them to call the shots.)
4. *Changed Business Definition.* If you believe that you must compete for the future through added value, you need to position yourself as a manager of care as well as a quantifiably high-quality provider.

Risk is simply no longer avoidable for most hospitals and health systems. From a marketing and business perspective, however, risk should not be undesirable. As any beginning business student—or business owner outside of nonprofit hospitals and for-profit doctors—can tell us, the first rule of genuinely competitive markets is "No risk, no reward." The provider or provider organization seeking to control their own destiny can look at the question from two perspectives.

From an insurer's perspective, as long as volume represents a source of income for the provider (who largely controls demand) at the insurer's expense, the insurer will seek to optimize control and influence over the care process, if not the provider. We must be quite clear on this point. In effect, the provider contracting with a payer on a fee-for-service basis is spending the payer's money. They will do so with little if any clinical autonomy or control. The less risk the provider accepts, the more interference from and involvement by the payer should be expected.

From the provider's perspective, the appropriate assumption of risk offers the opportunity for the provider to systematically improve the efficiency and effectiveness of the healthcare through the alignment of financial incentives. Such incentives can, if adopted by the practitioners whom it will effect and applied in a context of quality improvement, reinforce clinical behaviors that benefit the patient, the provider, the employer, and the payer.

The fundamental impetus behind risk-shifting and risk-sharing arrangements should be the intent of giving physicians empowerment and incentives to control variation in practice patterns and resource management to the extent that such variation is unwarranted and wasteful. And the literature suggests that a good deal of such variation is just that. Williamson, Goldschmidt, and Jillson (1979) documented common medical practices in three internal medicine subspecialties and found that fewer than 10 percent of the practices were based on the results of published medical research. Other studies cited by James (1993) suggest that "80 to 90 percent of common medical practices have no basis in published scientific research." Such variations in practice patterns suggest that healthcare, perhaps to a greater extent than any other sector of our economy, can gain both efficiencies and effectiveness by systematically and continuously addressing quality waste.

Large and Small Area Variation Analysis

Particularly since the publication of results from the National Demonstration Project for Quality in Healthcare nearly a decade ago, the literature now inarguably quantifies that healthcare is not exempt from the notion of quality waste and the intent of the quality-improvement movement that has transformed other industries. The notion of providing financial incentive to eliminate such waste appears not only practical and warranted but essential. Well before the National Demonstration Project, Wennberg and Gittelsohn (1982) published studies on small area variation analysis, arguing that variations of costs and utilization of healthcare services in various communities, even within the same region, has more to do with "the number of physicians there, their medical specialties, and the procedures they prefer than with the health of the residents."

The bottom line is that rates for the three most common surgical procedures (hysterectomy, prostatectomy, and tonsillectomy) in the highest use communities are six times those of communities with the lowest rates (Dartmouth Medical School 1999). Moreover, despite the use of clinical pathways and the national benchmarks such variations may be widening. Birkmeyer et al. (1998) reported that procedures with the highest variation profiles (lower extremity revascularization, carotid endarterectomy, back surgery, and radical prostatectomy) varied across the regions they studied by factors of 6.5 to 10.1. Perhaps more alarmingly, not only do these highly variant procedures represent some of the most risky for patients to undergo, but Birkmeyer's study (1998) concluded that "rates of 'discretionary' procedures are the most variable."

Consider the implication for a typical community hospital. Virtually everyone simultaneously finds themselves hampered by financial incentives, including per-case or diagnosis-related group (DRG) arrangements, under FFS payment. These incentives directly conflict with the demonstrated opportunities to reduce inappropriate and unwarranted procedures. Worse, generally dominated by the private practice of medicine, these same hospitals are increasingly subjected to the fragmenting pressures for physicians to perform procedures in their offices or attain ownership in free-standing centers in order to compensate for declining fee schedules. Whereas our society has historically looked to the community hospital to ensure quality and cost effectiveness through its medical staff bylaws and standards, in reality all but the most committed and courageous community hospital management teams and medical executive committees will find any meaningful level of utilization management or quality improvement well outside the borders of their will, intent, and incentives.

Variations in Resource Utilization

The implications of such variations in practice patterns are not limited to the social and external. They just as certainly and clearly reach into the hospitals where many of us work and most of us have received care. For instance, one hospital recently conducted an internal analysis of physician-directed resource utilization. Limiting the study to the use of those resources directly under the physician's control and adjusting for patient severity by both throwing out outliers and employing all payer DRGs, the hospital looked at variations between the more efficient practitioners and the less efficient across its top 20 (by dollar volume) DRGs. At the very least variations of 25 percent to 40 percent were observed. Most physicians, however, exceeded this range, and several varied by as much as 300 percent or more. Again, however, we find little to be surprised by here. Deep and broad veins of inefficiency and ineffectiveness are well-mapped in the healthcare literature (Williamson, Goldschmidt, and Jillson 1979; James 1993). A recent and remarkable study updated an analysis of prescription drug use problems in the United States (Ernst and Grizzle 2001). It estimates that drug misuse costs the economy more than $177 billion each year and is responsible for roughly 50 percent of every dollar spent on prescription drugs in the first place! The implications, of course, extend beyond the financial: the estimated number of patient deaths from drug misuse has increased from 198,000 in 1995 to 218,000 in 2000.

Quality Improvement

Few physicians today would equate capitation with quality or quality improvement. For most it smacks of some combination of rationing, inappropriate shifting of the insurance function, and an attempt to reduce provider compensation. Unfortunately in many instances and markets that perception is all too accurate. Unfortunate too is the fact that these physicians have learned only half the lesson: this may be how capitation has been used, but it need not reflect how it can work.

Indemnity insurers seeking to introduce managed care products rather than actually transform themselves into managed care organizations latched onto capitation as a means of fixing, and thereby controlling, their costs. Consistent with their culture and competitive practice of succeeding based on their capability for risk avoidance rather than their capacity for risk management, they reasoned that by carving out large chunks of their risk they would be able to protect administrative costs and more reliably project profitable outcomes. Many subsequently capitated physician groups with little or no infrastructure and less accountability, groups that were either too small or immature to bear the financial pressures that were to ensue. Few required feedback in terms of encounter or performance data. Like drivers following each other too closely in the fog, chain reactions of failure and economic collisions typically followed.

If we did not know better then, we certainly should now. Capitation as a cost-containment strategy does not work. As the result of work by such people as Berwick we know that successful risk-based contracting relies on "the system of care in which it is used" as well as on "the competence and willingness of the doctors and the delivery system to improve their own work." Here we arrive at the heart of the matter: payment mechanism is a tool to support strategic objective and cultural commitment, and finance is a means to an end, not the end itself. We know that when properly employed in provider-sponsored delivery systems, risk-based contracting "can encourage better decisions and facilitate the productive redesign of systems for the delivery of care" by providing "a rational financial contest that vastly increases the opportunities . . . to make changes that result in better and more efficient care for patients and communities" (Berwick 1996).

While we will examine the tactical requirements of success under capitation later, the strategic requirement is simultaneously simple and profound—an organization built on the premise that quality improvement represents the only sustainable cost-control strategy in healthcare. Thus, the real question that today's managed care environment poses is not whether to accept risk, but whether we have the will to create the circumstances that will allow us to use it to reinforce our organizational mission and purpose. In short, risk-based contracting can actually provide both the means and the incentive for an organization to truly provide the highest quality at the lowest cost.

Enlightened Self-interest and Preservation

For those who remain unconvinced by the positive arguments for risk contracting, we offer a negative one: self-interest. In FFS markets, particularly once inpatient days are reduced from loosely to moderately or well-managed levels, payers can primarily rely only upon discounting physicians and hospitals to control costs. This strategy can only be expected to continually further fragment these indemnity-based markets as more and more physicians, seeing fee schedules being slashed to levels at or below Medicare, add outpatient diagnostic and therapeutic services typically provided by the hospital. Goaded to short-term self-interest and seeking to restore income levels, physicians in such markets will have little time for and less interest in a systems approach to quality care. Moreover, while some of this activity probably belongs in the physician office in the first place, physicians will likely find that they must run faster and faster to stay in the same financial place. In other words, adding such services is really only a temporary fix that will leave them more frustrated with medicine than ever and likely make variations in discretionary and office-based procedures continue to grow.

In conclusion, regardless of the reason, providers looking for sustainable success strategies will need to turn to some type of risk-based contracting. Of course, to do so successfully requires the appropriate strategy and infrastructure, both of which must be based on a solid understanding of insurance risk.

INVERTING THE ECONOMIC PARADIGM

As we learned from experience with DRGs almost 20 years ago, risk-based contracts impart to the provider organization a financial incentive to measure and manage costs, requiring in turn changes in an organization's infrastructure to support more efficient and effective clinical and managerial behaviors. Figure 4.1 diagrams the new economic relationships among volume, fixed and variable costs, and revenue under capitation, the quintessence of managed care.

In the economic model of FFS payments charges for units of service represent a source of funds, whereas in a capitated environment those same charges become a source of costs. FFS revenues increase proportionately with volume per person. Past the break-even point profits are earned and typically increase with higher volume. Capitation inverts this logic: Profits are earned at low volumes of service per person and decrease with higher volumes past the break-even point. Thus, providers approach breakeven from the other direction—by decreasing volumes or at least through resource utilization.

Common to both FFS and capitation is the fact that revenues increase with the number of persons served given constant volume of services per person. The critical difference is that under capitation the

Figure 4.1: Reversing Incentives by Inverting the Economic Paradigm

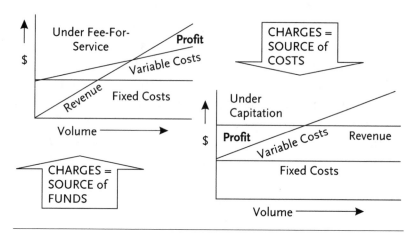

currency of the provider realm shifts from units of services to covered lives. Of course it is still true under capitation that to attract and retain persons to the provider's panel (or population served) the volume and quality of service must pass the test of the marketplace.

The Fixed and Variable Effects of Cost Management

Interestingly, the nature of cost-control incentives differs under FFS and capitation regimens. Consider first variable costs per unit of service. The provider reimbursed on an FFS basis will gain more by lowering variable costs per unit of output than under capitation. This is because under FFS reimbursement not only is the variable-cost reduction spread over higher volumes per person, but the provider actually gains an extra increment of profitability (equal to the price) on each additional unit of volume supplied relative to capitation; the clinician responds to the incentive of a lower variable production cost per unit.

On the other hand, reductions in volume-independent fixed costs per person affect profitability the same way under capitation or FFS arrangements only if you assume that reductions in per-person costs do not induce providers to expand the size of their enrolled populations.

However, if lower per-person costs are assumed to create incentives to expand enrollment, lowering per-person costs will depend on the relative size of the average profit per person under the two payment regimens. In a market with capitation payments that are relatively generous compared to FFS equivalents the incentives to lower these per-person, volume-fixed costs will be greater under capitation regimens.

The greatest difference, of course, between cost-control incentives under capitation and FFS payment systems is with respect to managing volumes. The capitated provider essentially loses an amount equal to the variable cost of a service multiplied by the number of persons served for every unit increase in volume per person (e.g., one additional specialty referral per enrollee). Alternatively, the FFS provider gains an amount equal to the contribution margin (price minus variable cost) multiplied by the number of persons served for every unit increase in volume per person. If increased volume per person encourages new enrollment of average risk (i.e., healthcare costs per person), this demand response will exacerbate the losses under capitation arrangements and enhance the gains under FFS systems.

In summary, the paradigm shift in cost management experienced in the move from FFS to capitation payment is concentrated on the new incentive to reduce the volume of services per person and control the costs of volume-fixed infrastructure associated with serving a defined population. We can argue, however, that the provider's incentive to reduce variable costs per unit of volume is actually weakened under capitation arrangements because the additional profit from unit-cost reductions is lower than under FFS systems because each unit of volume earns the price of that service under FFS payment. Because capitation payment severs this link between volume of service and price the gain from achieving variable-cost economies is mitigated.

THE SOURCES AND STRUCTURE OF RISK

Regardless of the payment mechanism used in a risk-based contract, providers need to thoroughly understand both the nature of insurance risk and how that risk uniformly structures itself within an insured population. On one hand, transitioning from an undifferentiated role as provider of care to the value-added role of manager of care requires that physicians and hospitals accept risk. On the other, the financial risk that providers accept should generally be limited to their own efficiency and effectiveness, limit or exclude risk beyond their control, and be adjusted for the enrolled population. Understanding the respective sources of risk will assist providers in assuming and, perhaps as importantly, avoiding risk appropriately. Understanding the structure of risk will assist in managing risk tactically once it is assumed.

The Aggregated Risk Pool

The term risk pool seems so appropriate, so suitably figurative. Just as streams empty into rivers and rivers into lakes or oceans, various tributaries of risk converge, intermingle, and empty into a pool. Moreover, once they have blended it is generally anything but easy to segregate them again. Herein lies a large part of the challenge of cost analysis and management strategies we will discuss later: How do we calculate with any precision where, for instance, patient-generated demand for a procedure or drug ends and physician-driven demand begins? For now we simply note that some of these sources derive from factors under the provider's direct or indirect control, whereas others clearly do not.

Several sources contribute to the aggregated financial risk.

The Enrolled Population

As we will see, commercial enrollees not only have a different total cost structure than, say, Medicare or Medicaid enrollees, but they each use a different configuration of services. For instance, a percentage of total Medicare patients will use more of most specialty services and obviously fewer of others (e.g., obstetrics). While total PMPM expenses increase for both primary care and specialty services as might be expected, specialist costs for the Medicare population increase disproportionately so that specialist costs represent a great percentage of total physician expenses.

The Contract Portfolio

Within a commercial risk pool specific employer types and sizes will have different risk-cost profiles. Benefit structure will not only influence the totality of costs in the pool (versus how much of the costs are borne by the members), but also whether members are given incentive to use less expensive and resource intense sites of care (such as primary care physicians or urgent-care clinics) or more expensive sites (such as consultants and emergency departments) for particular problems. Moreover, sociodemographic and other characteristics of the population selecting a given product will significantly influence a pool's size and nature.

Case Variability

Even within a commercial population where employers are grouped by size and class or professional category, no two firms will have the same mix of employees who are well, who have some type of chronic but managed disease, and those few who represent potentially "catastrophic" claims. Moreover, no two firms will have the same distribution of enrollees by age and sex.

Age and sex factors have significant influence over cost and are often used as the primary predictor of utilization. Note that health plan expenses vary not only by age cohort but by gender as well. Moreover, expenses also vary by service type by age and sex.

Utilization Patterns

Although the population, specific portfolio, and mix of cases will shape risk, healthcare providers still exhibit wide variations in practice patterns across all types of services. We have already seen wide variations in surgical rates for different procedures. Inpatient utilization rates may vary even more widely.

Figure 4.2 reflects various measures of anticipated inpatient utilization for a commercial and Medicare population respectively. Note the disparity between "loosely" managed inpatient care (typical of

Figure 4.2: Utilization Management Guidlines

Commercial Inpatient

| | Outcomes When Managed . . . | | |
	Loosely	Moderately	Well
Admissions	79.90	69.79	51.20
Length of Stay	5.09	4.18	2.17
Days/1,000	406.60	275.00	139.00
Days as % of Loose	—	68%	34%

Medicare-aged Inpatient

| | Outcomes When Managed . . . | | |
	Loosely	Moderately	Well
Admissions	288.30	215.47	149.80
Length of Stay	8.27	6.96	.69
Days/1,000	2,385.00	1,500.00	702.10
Days as % of Loose	—	63%	29%

fee-for-service markets dominated by little if any meaningful managed care) and "well" managed care (most notably those markets with at least 30% HMO penetration).

As discussed above, utilization will be driven by several factors well outside the physician's or health system's control. However, much seems difficult to understand, primarily because of quality waste, lack of coordination, and inefficient practice patterns.

Cost or Price Per Unit

What accountants refer to as the cost of goods sold can and usually does vary widely from region to region. Nevertheless, within a given region the individual provider has significant influence over such costs.

The Structure of Risk

Interestingly, in any statistically significant pool we can actually draw what financial risk looks like in a typical risk pool, characterizing its key features by its behavior. We can use that predicted behavior to craft corresponding cost-management strategies as we will see below. This will surprise no one familiar with the Pareto principle, although typically the results are skewed even beyond the 80:20 rule.

Determining Statistical Significance

Before examining structure, however, we will look briefly at the concept of statistical significance. We can only predict the structure or distribution of costs in a statistically significant risk pool.

As demonstrated in Figure 4.3, as membership rises from a nominal level, such as 100 members, to a considerably larger level, such as 10,000, the likelihood that costs will end up at budgeted levels rises from a mere 30 percent to a more reasonable 90 percent, all other factors being equal. At this level costs are as likely to vary by at least 25 percent in either direction as they are to be on budget. Conversely, however, as membership grows the likelihood that the budget will be missed by 25 percent or more either way decreases from an unacceptable 30 percent to a barely measurable level. In other words, the slopes of the distribution curve steepen and predictability increases.

Distribution of Expenses

What can we expect in a pool of insureds that achieves statistical significance? A small minority of members will generate the majority of expenses, and the great majority of members will generate very nominal expenses. For instance, as few as .1 percent of the members will likely generate 10 percent of the costs, and 5 percent will generate nearly 60 percent of the costs! This simple statistical principal has profound implications for underwriting (or avoiding) and rating risk, sharing appropriately adjusted risk, and in particular matching risk-management strategies to specific population groups.

Figure 4.3: Statistical Significance—The Effect of Pool Size on Probability

At 100 members . . .

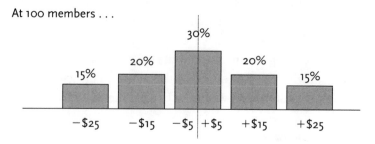

At 1,000 members . . .

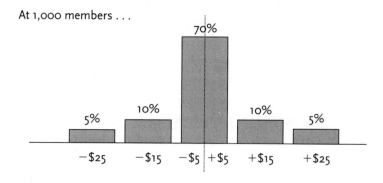

At 10,000 members . . .

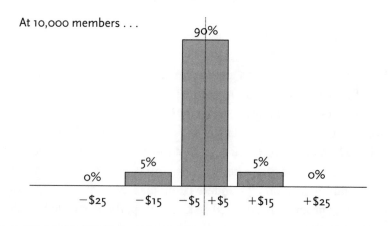

COST STRUCTURE IMPLICATIONS

The cost structure or distribution of expenses described above carries significant implications for providers contracting at risk, particularly under capitation because of the assumption of risk, specifically (1) underwriting or assuming and rating risk in general, (2) underwriting small groups specifically, and (3) premium setting and pricing or risk sharing. By examining these activities we are by no means advocating that providers seek to have any involvement in them—unless of course they are owners of a health plan. However, providers will only want to assume risk proportionate to the payment they expect to receive. Because the payment will be otherwise fixed, providers negotiating risk-based contracts will want to understand how the health plan estimates and prices for this risk and be assured that any adjustments in premium to the plan based on risk are proportionately and fairly reflected in adjustments in payment to the provider.

The last of these major implications concerns the management of risk. As we emphasized in chapter 3, the provider organization accepting risk becomes, in effect, a managed care organization. Having negotiated and executed a contract at an appropriately adjusted fixed price, the provider organization must implement risk-management strategies designed specifically for the three different population segments within any risk pool that will be discussed later. For the most part no single solution exists for managing all three segments.

Underwriting and Rating Risk

We can arrange the rate-setting approaches used by health plans according to the degree to which they credibly predict revenues and expenses (see Figure 4.4). Other things being equal, the provider is taking less risk by accepting capitation reimbursement for a group of contracts as the group's rating credibility increases. The hierarchy starts with community-rated groups, whose rates are based on the average amount for a larger population that is not necessarily comparable to the specific contract group. Moving up the ladder of rating credibility, class-adjusted community rating, prospective

Figure 4.4: Predictive Abilities of Various Rating Methodologies[*]

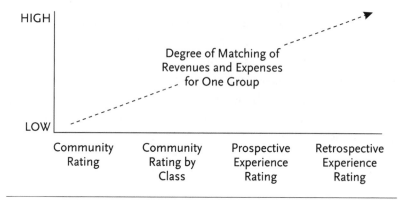

experience rating, and retrospective experience rating are plan rate-setting methodologies that progressively reduce the actuarial risk assumed by the provider in accepting capitation reimbursement. In brief, the rating methodologies function as follows.

- Community spreads costs and savings across entire risk pool (e.g., community); inclusive of the entire community experience
- Community by class adjusts rates for group characteristics (e.g., age and sex)
- Adjusted community further refines rates on a prospective basis based on past experience.
- Experience based adjusts rates based on experience factors specific to the insured pool and exclusive of others' experience.

Underwriting Issues Specific to Small Groups

Although the definition of what constitutes a small group varies from payer to payer and state to state, most states regulate and closely oversee how health plans underwrite and rate smaller employers. Carriers typically medically underwrite small groups, seeking to carefully identify which groups represent acceptable levels of risk based on pre-existing conditions and which do not. Underwriting criteria employed by health plans with regard to small groups usually include the following.

- *Employer or employee relationship preclusions.* Payers may seek to limit or preclude nonimmediate family members, particularly those working part time, out of concern that such relatives are only employed as a means of accessing health insurance.
- *Minimum (or total group) participation.* Usually health plans will preclude any kind of side-by-side offering, requiring that their plan cover all insureds.
- *Minimum employer contribution.* Unless the employer pays for a substantial portion of the premium, the health plan will assume that only those employees who need coverage the most will enroll for it.
- *Medical underwriting.* The plan will likely screen for pre-existing conditions by individually medically underwriting members. Whereas prior to the Health Insurance Portability and Accountability Act payers could accept or reject members, today plans can only use such information to adjust the premium it charges to the employer.

For provider organizations contemplating acceptance of capitated contracts for small groups the most important consideration to remember is that the major risk-avoidance effects of medical underwriting effectively "wear off" after one year. After two years individual medical underwriting has virtually no predictable value.

Setting Premium and Pricing Providers

If you accept the argument that managed care contracting represents a vertical integration strategy for both provider and payer, it follows that the parties have a reciprocal and vested interest in each other's pricing strategies. Specifically: (1) the payer should want to see that providers are properly compensated and ensure as part of their proper compensation that they will not be unfairly or inappropriately put at risk[1]; and (2) the provider will understand that the payer represents his or her channel of distribution in the marketplace and that the payer's pricing strategy accordingly becomes by default the provider's.[2]

In both instances the integrative nature of risk-based contracting and the direct link between premium and provider payment that results make appropriate a careful consideration of the risk structure and behavior. In particular the payment mechanism and payment level agreed upon should consider the effects of:

- rating adjustments on the flow of funds, ensuring that providers are compensated for the risk they accept; and
- health status, recognizing that self-reported health status may represent the most effective means of projecting patient demand on a delivery system (see Addendum A).

The argument that providers and payers have an enlightened self-interest in each other's financial success in the marketplace runs counter to the behaviors of most providers and most payers in most markets today. In general, plans seek to leverage their purchasing power by negotiating provider fees to as low a level as possible, and providers do the opposite. Perhaps for the majority of relationships such a posture seems both reasonable and necessary. However, given the serious, integrative, and strategic nature of risk-based contracting, we would argue to providers that they re-examine this perspective for those payers who are most critical to maintaining or expanding market share. Conversely, of course, we would make the same argument to payers.

CARE MANAGEMENT STRATEGIES

We turn now to what may represent the most significant implication for a provider-sponsored managed care organization: care management. This is, after all, supposed to be what managed care is all about.

As noted earlier, in any given risk pool a small minority of members generates a disproportionate share of the medical expenses. In a typical commercial pool anywhere from 2.5 percent to 5 percent of the enrollees will likely generate approximately 50 percent or more of the health plan's costs. A second enrollee segment will also generate costs disproportionate to their representation in the pool, although not at a rate anywhere near as dramatic as the first segment. This segment, representing roughly 14 to 17 percent of the total population, can be expected to incur perhaps 30 percent of the total costs. Together these first two segments will represent no more than 20 percent of the enrollees but at least 80 percent—and quite possibly 90 percent—of the costs, embodying the Pareto principle. Finally, a third segment consisting of the overwhelming majority of enrollees will represent the minority of costs. If we target our attention to the care management implications of this cost distribution and requirements of the specific enrollee segments, two different tactical approaches are suggested.

Organizational

Organizational tactics primarily relate to delivery system and benefit design. Delivery system design includes the selection of providers based on some combination of access, quality, and cost. The managed care organization should tailor the design of the delivery system to the specific population it intends to serve. For instance, panel selection for a commercial population will vary significantly from delivery system design for a Medicaid population. Both would likely vary in the panel of providers that would be employed for a Medicare population. Within a plan type, however, delivery system design overarches and applies to all three of the enrollee segments discussed above.

Benefit design includes cost-sharing strategies and the use of co-payments and deductibles. Provider organizations, of course, will have little influence over benefit design. They should, however, understand it and anticipate differences in utilization levels that benefit design is likely to influence.

Programmatic

Programmatic tactics include approaches familiar to nearly any reader with any managed care experience. Each is considered in more detail in chapter 6. Each program has a use specific to one, and no more than two, enrollee segments.

The utilization review or medical management programs so popular with third parties can be very effective for two of the three enrollee segments. Certainly these tools will be applied to the vast majority of the enrollees. However, for at least 50 percent of the costs such an approach will have limited if any value.

Wellness and prevention activities, including health screening and education, should again be targeted to the two segments representing the majority of employees. Again, however, such activities address only one portion of the plan's costs and, unlike utilization review activities, do not typically have a short-term payoff.

Disease management programs will be offered to those members with chronic health problems and will require the adoption of clinical protocol by participating physicians. Case management will concern itself with high-cost episodes of care, seeking to optimize the mix of available services and recognize the multiple needs of patients with the most serious health problems.

To be truly effective in targeting the minority of enrollees using the majority of costs, large case management efforts require intense, dedicated resources expended over an extended period. While significant benefit can be derived from addressing and coordinating primarily medical concerns, the needs of these patients extend to virtually every other aspect of their lives and support of these people must go well beyond what would be construed by most medical directors as medically necessary. As such, few organizations have marshaled the teams required for comprehensively addressing what may well represent 50 to 60 percent of a health plan's expenses.

In light of the tactical complexity and comprehensive perspective required of a true managed care approach, it is not surprising that what has passed for managed care—risk avoidance or transfer, deeply discounting providers, restricting access, and slowing payments—has been less than effective. Moreover, where this approach has achieved some effectiveness in the past—primarily in driving down unit costs and reducing utilization of inpatient days and the most expensive outpatient procedures—the effectiveness of such tactics will almost inevitably diminish as the underlying causes of healthcare inflation have shifted.

DETERMINING PAYMENT ADEQUACY: THE FLOW AND ALLOCATION OF FUNDS

The above discussion sets the stage for determining (or at least considering) the adequacy of payment to providers by reviewing the various elements of the risk pool, evaluating the implications of the structure of that risk pool, and contemplating the organization's capacity for managing that risk through an appropriate configuration of strategies. By next examining how funds flow through a health plan we can finally turn to the question of payment levels and examine the ultimate risk-based payment mechanism, capitation.

Role of the Actuary

In recent years a significant number of useful reference publications have become available for considering and benchmarking the financial performance measures we consider in the following sections. Such relatively generic references, however, cannot address the specifics of local health plan practices. As such, we find the judicious and selective use of an actuarial firm with experience in a given market helpful. The key advantages that such assistance brings, and that will not likely be otherwise available, include the following (Axene, 1992).

Obtain Normative Community Use or Cost Profile

The actuary can assist with profiling a particular community in terms of both the labor force demographic mix and evaluation of current levels of utilization management.

Estimate Effect of Ultimately Managed Delivery System

By estimating the effect of best-practice utilization programs, the resultant shifts in patterns of care, and the most competitive pricing available the actuary can estimate the effect of the overall delivery system on overall use and cost.

Project Effect of the Proposed Managed Care System

Using the current profile of the community as one measure and the ultimate use-cost levels that might be achieved as the other, the actuary can help project the effect of a proposed managed care system in terms of copayments and other benefit design changes as well as the potential effectiveness of the contemplated delivery system.

Anticipate Enrollment Distribution

Given what is known of options available to a certain group of employees in terms of delivery system and cost sharing or other incentives, the actuary can project the distribution of the labor force demographic mix into different health plans or benefit designs.

Develop Cost Models and Forecasts

By changing such variables as plan design, cost, and delivery system organization, the actuary can provide a variety of cost models and forecasts to simulate alternative scenarios.

Providers with years of experience in risk-based contracts will no doubt feel a minimal need for such support. Those who are new to risk-based contracts (or where one or more of the variables has significantly changed) will probably do well to seek actuarial support in modeling the financial constructs that follow.

The Flow of Funds

The flow of funds begins with the employer and passes through the HMO to various providers. In most instances the following mechanisms apply.

Premium Payment

The employer pays a premium to the health plan that will be adjusted for age, sex, and possibly other risk factors as discussed above.

Plan Retention

The health plan will retain a portion of the premium to cover the costs of administration, out-of-area claims (for which the locally contracting provider organization would not be responsible), tertiary care services that are not part of the contract (e.g., transplantation), and any specialty services that are carved out (e.g., behavioral health). Additionally, the plan will retain funds for any benefit riders not included in the contract (e.g., dental, pharmacy, or vision care).

Under a fully capitated arrangement the health plan distributes payment for all remaining medical services on a prepaid or prospective basis. Because its medical costs are fixed at this point it can retain as its profit margin whatever portion of the premium it is not required to pay to providers.

Under a partially capitated arrangement the health plan typically capitates the provider organization for all physician services and perhaps for associated ancillary outpatient services such as laboratory work and radiology. The plan then sets aside reserves for services for which it is at risk.

Under virtually any other arrangement the health plan is basically compensating providers on an FFS basis. The plan will be required to establish appropriate reserves and will only be able to estimate its actual profit for any given period until it can reliably determine its incurred-but-not-reported claims.

Provider Payments

As noted, under a fully capitated arrangement the provider organization receives payment for all remaining medical expenses. It must then allocate the capitation for hospital and physician services. For illustrative purposes we use a hospital fund for inpatient and outpatient services, respectively, and a physician fund is similarly divided into estimated allocations for PCPS, specialists, and hospital-based physicians (anesthesiologists, radiologists, pathologists, and emergency room physicians are often paid on salary by the hospital). The organization will determine the appropriate allocation of funds by using an approach similar to that of HMOs: determining first payment mechanisms and then payment levels (discussed below). In this latter task the organization's method will likely differ from the health plan's, although its outcome must be essentially the same.

Reinsurance

For high-cost cases that exceed specified stop-loss levels, either the health plan will provide (or providers will need to obtain) reinsurance.

DETERMINING APPROPRIATE PAYMENT LEVELS

How do we determine payment reasonableness? How do we allocate dollars reasonably and responsibly?

Budget estimates, which can be found in various publications and are generally well worth referencing, can provide a helpful guideline. Many providers, and even some payers, use such generic approaches, even without the support and assistance of an actuarial firm. As has been often observed, however, a practice can be quite common and still be inappropriate. We suggest, rather, that the only fiscally responsible method for building an appropriate budget is from the ground up, as we discuss next.

Determining Payment Reasonableness

Whether to the health plan from the employer or to the provider from the health plan, we have already seen that a number of factors should influence the allocation of funds and contribute to determining payment reasonableness. Particularly when considering a capitated payment, the provider cannot consider simply the total payment—even in comparison with a payment from another HMO in the same market—without a consideration of at least the following factors.

Identification and Definition of Covered Services

Virtually no two at-risk contracts will contain exactly the same terms. The risk-based contract must specify both clinical (down to the CPT code level) and administrative services to be provided, and define "out of area" and who is responsible for coverage when the member is more than 25 or 50 miles away (as defined).

Underlying Utilization Assumptions

As discussed, a plan can make significantly variant assumptions about the utilization level for any given service and how much those levels can be affected by the provider. It is critical to understand current and proposed utilization levels by covered service. Utilization assumptions or projections will generally be built upon a consideration of: (1) current community norms for the type of population to be enrolled; and (2) capability of the contracting provider organization to influence or change the utilization patterns for each of the contracted clinical services.

Payment Adjustments

Whatever the particular plan's practices and policies with regard to underwriting and rating risk, the provider need not (and probably should not) seek to influence them. However, the provider should understand them and be assured that the provider's payment is adjusted exactly as is the health plan's. Minimally such adjustments should include:

- demographic mix adjustment (age-sex);
- benefit design adjustment (copayments or lack thereof);

- medical underwriting adjustments (for small groups); and
- experience factor (for large groups).

Additionally, two other comparatives can be extremely useful as a means of providing a benchmark: (1) historic experience with the HMO; and (2) experience with other HMOs serving similar populations with similar benefit design.

Underlying Fee Schedule Assumptions

Whereas the above steps will employ reasonably—though not fully—quantitative approaches, the final step of establishing the underlying fee schedule assumptions will remain a purely qualitative process no matter what quantitative tools are used. It is largely here that the principles of negotiation outlined in chapter 5 come into play. In a larger and more profound sense it is here that the core philosophy and business mentality of the payer makes itself patently and perfectly manifest.

As with an employer who seeks to pay his or her employees as little as possible, the payer who selects and contracts with providers strictly based on cost makes clear the lack of value placed on performance or worker satisfaction. Such a provider demonstrates that systems thinking has no place and recognizes no particular relationship among provider satisfaction, member satisfaction, membership stability, and financial performance of the provider organization.

More enlightened negotiations will likely begin with some kind of quantifiable market data, deriving negotiated payments as either: (1) a percentage of a recognized relative value scale (e.g., Medicare's resource-based relative value system); or (2) a percentile of market rates (either private or commercially available).

In the end, of course, any service is worth what the payer will pay and a seller will sell for. However, balancing provider market share on the one hand and payer volume on the other can allow a reasonably objective and impersonal discussion to be held and a fair conclusion to be reached.

The real worth of a provider or provider organization only begins with its ability to attract patients. It culminates in the organization's performance in working with the payer to assist in managing costs.

Just as pay for performance has permeated other industries, it is inevitable that it will do so in healthcare. Systems-thinking provider and payer organizations across the country have already begun implementing pay-for-performance measures. Addendum B provides examples of various categories of pay for performance–based payment mechanisms.

Establishing the Budget

The above steps allow us to produce anticipated utilization rates and defined costs per unit of service for all healthcare services. Multiplying total utilization by unit cost gives total cost. A comprehensive and useful budget:

- delineates services and provides the unit of measure;
- provides targeted or budgeted utilization rates;
- sites the unit cost for each service component;
- calculates the gross cost/payment PMPM;
- indicates copayments for which a member, rather than the plan, is responsible; and
- reflects the net payment to provider (the gross cap minus the effective PMPM value of the copayment).

Note that despite the fact that payments are reflected as PMPM figures, providers are not necessarily capitated for all these services; these services are simply budgeted this way, which conveniently does two things. First, it allows us to create the ultimate flexible budget. The per-member costs (within a range) for health services should not vary to any significant degree with membership. This method of budgeting is incomparably beneficial to using absolute numbers.

Second, it facilitates retrospective analysis of financial performance by allowing us to determine the degree to which a variance from budget derived from either a variance in utilization or a variation in unit cost. Unless we build the budget at this level we cannot meaningfully analyze the financial performance of the plan.

Finally, we should point out that total provider payment derives payments by both the plan and the member. Also, capitation rates for PCPS would not necessarily reflect all payment to PCPS insofar as PCPS would likely be allowed to bill for some services on an FFS basis.

Developing a Multicontract Budget

The above discussion builds a budget for a typical HMO. But what about the provider organization seeking to build a budget based on contracts with several HMOS?

Consider the example of a start-up PHO that is contracting for physician and outpatient services. Income statements show three plans totaling 50,702 contracted member months. The revenue sources are the capitation payment and estimated reinsurance payments, which vary by plan and the inflow from coordination of benefits or subrogation with other payers. Incentive payments (e.g., bonuses for positive utilization and medical expense performance) and interest income are not present in this situation for any of the three plans. The budgeted expense in this example includes:

- PCP capitation ($9.84) and a budget incentive of 10 percent of that capitation (98 cents). We should make two extremely important notes here. First, the budget's construction indicates that the PHO intends to pay out an amount up to this budgeted incentive based on the actual performance of the individual PCPS without regard to how the organization itself does. Such an approach is critical to establishing and maintaining credibility with, and the support of, the PCPS. Only through such fiscal policy does the organization "walk the talk" of being primary care based. Second, the PHO elected to use a positive incentive, not a withhold. Again, the budget reflects the fiscal philosophy and principles of the organization. Consider, for instance, the implications for your own organization if you told a key employee, "Here's your market-based salary, but I'm going to withhold part of it just in case I need to spend it on something else." Withholds have the same effect on physicians.

- A capitation for selected specialty services and estimated FFS costs for other specialists. In fact, the capitation for specialists will likely vary based on differing copayments used by the health plans.
- The hospital capitation and a separate hospital FFS component. As an overall rule, we recommend only accepting capitation for services you directly provide and influence. In this instance, the hospital wished to share financial risk with the physicians as a philosophic stance.
- Administrative expenses budgeted for each plan or product line served by the PHO.

For our purposes the actual numbers are less important than the concepts highlighted in the example. For example, the PHO in plan A is simply a management support vehicle for the PCPs and specialists to contract on a mixed capitated and FFS basis with the health plan. In plans B and C, on the other hand, the physicians and the hospital are jointly at risk through the PHO for their share of the capitation. Administrative expense would include functions like general plan management, physician management support services, provider credentialing, member services, actuarial services, accounting and finance, and claims processing. The health plan products could be provided directly (sponsored) by the PHO itself, or the PHO might contract with an independent health plan or HMO. Certain services, such as actuarial services and claims processing, might be contracted out by the PHO (outsourced) or delivered in house, depending on the managerial and information systems capacity of the provider organization.

Guidelines for when Plans Will Share and Shift Risk

Later in this chapter we will examine why health plans will want to shift or share risk as much in the next several years as they have at any time in the last several years. In the interim, we can examine those conditions under which plans have historically sought to pass risk onto providers in times of higher medical inflation. As a general rule, health plans will find it to be in their economic and organizational best interests to shift the entire risk to providers in the following instances.

Lower Cost and Lower Margin Services

Most plans will not find it cost effective to attempt to employ third-party utilization review techniques or tools to manage down or control the majority of services by volume that represent the minority of costs.

More Difficult Populations (e.g., Medicaid)

For populations with unique delivery system requirements, such as Medicaid, health plans will probably look to provider-sponsored organizations unless they themselves specialize in these populations.

More Difficult Services (e.g., Mental Health and Chemical Dependency)

For niche services, such as behavioral health or reference laboratory services, health plans will probably carve out the total costs and seek to shift the risk to a provider that can meet these special needs.

In order to align financial interests providers and health plans should seek to somehow share risk in the following situations.

Higher Cost and Margin Services (e.g., Inpatient Days, Outpatient Surgery)

In different ways both the health plan and the provider influence the cost and utilization levels of higher cost services such as inpatient days or outpatient surgical cases.

Achievement of Qualitative Goals

As health plans seek to differentiate themselves through the kind of third-party endorsements represented by National Committee on Quality Assurance accreditation or ratings they will provide financial incentives to physicians and hospitals to encourage the achievement of standards established by such organizations. Numerous plans also provide such financial rewards for goals established by plans to compete in local markets. For instance, it is not uncommon for health plans to reward physicians for maintaining open practices, achieving specific patient satisfaction levels, or complying with clinical protocol such as formularies.

Sophisticated contractual arrangement will tangibly acknowledge that some risk is appropriately maintained by the plan, while some risk should be shifted to the provider and other risk should be shared by both plan and provider. Consider the example of a health plan that both shifts risk to and shares risk with a provider, capitating provider organizations for all physician and outpatient lab and radiology services. The plan retains the risk for inpatient utilization as well as for outpatient pharmaceuticals but establishes a fund for each of these services out of which it shares savings with the provider organization. It also establishes a third fund for rewarding quality improvement. The health plan in question will only execute risk-based contracts with provider-sponsored organizations, not with individuals. Additionally, such organizations must meet certain minimum requirements established by the HMO. Primarily, the provider organization must be built around a multispecialty panel of physicians capable of establishing "a rational delivery system of care" as well as administering risk-based contracts. The health plan is indifferent as to whether a hospital participates in the provider organization but in any event insists on maintaining the hospital contract itself.

Such an arrangement seems particularly enlightened. First and foremost it recognizes that physicians control the majority of resources but that they can only do so meaningfully in the context of a locally organized, self-sponsored delivery system. Second, it responsively shifts risk, adjusted for both variations in benefit design and case variability, for services most directly under the physician's control. Rather than shifting, it shares the risk of hospital utilization while passing on the benefits of managing pharmaceuticals without requiring the provider organization to attempt to build the infrastructure of a pharmacy benefits management program. Third, it provides positive financial incentives for achievement of qualitative goals that benefit the member and differentiate the plan. Increasingly health plans will employ such pay-for-performance risk arrangements with providers.

CAPITATION

As noted earlier, the fact that the above budgets assess healthcare costs or payments in terms of a PMPM measure does not necessarily mean that they capitate all services. Nevertheless, an in-depth understanding of these budgets does require a basic understanding of capitation.

Definition and Calculation

Capitation is a method for prospectively paying providers an amount per member per time period for specified services regardless of actual use level. Typically expressed in dollars and cents PMPM, occasionally capitation payments will be expressed as a per-member-per-year number (PMPY). Calculating a monthly capitation rate is a simple matter of following three basic mathematic steps.

Determining Use Rate

Use rates expressed in units per thousand (population) are derived by dividing the total number of anticipated encounters per year by the population. Thus, if we expected a total of 3,100 office visits for a population of 1,000 members, the use rate is:

$$3,100/1,000 = 3.1 \text{ visits PMPY.}$$

Multiplying the Use Rate by the Unit Cost

Multiplying the office visit rate of 3.1 by an average office visit cost/payment of $52 provides us with an annual cost of:

$$3.1 \text{ visits per year} \times \$52 \text{ per visit} = \$161.20 \text{ PMPY.}$$

Deriving a Monthly Payment Level

To derive a PMPM rate divide the annual cost by 12:

$$\$161.20/12 \text{ months} = \$14.43 \text{ PMPM.}$$

The above formula can then be applied to all provider services whether for physicians with commercial or Medicare populations or for hospital services.

Effects of Copayments

When plan benefit design requires the member to pay for a portion of an episode of care, the industry refers to such payment as a copay. Unlike deductibles, copayment amounts are not cumulative. They effectively do two things. First, by definition they shift some portion of the cost of the visit to the member. Thus, total provider capitation will be a function of both plan payment (fixed relative to the total number of visits, as we have seen) and member copayments (variable relative to the number of visits). More to the point, copayments affect utilization, which is the point of their introduction.

For most services copayments effectively reduce utilization. While the exact effect certainly varies based on the population, local consumer preferences, the specific service, overall plan design, and other likely factors that combine to reduce the predictability of the effect, one plan's experience with office copayments seems to support the traditional perception that the most dramatic effect of copayments occurs between $0 and some nominal figure.

Providers concerned with the incentives that capitated arrangements create for overutilization will certainly prefer contracts with plans requiring some type of member copayment.

Guidelines for Using and Transitioning to Capitation

We have already covered the majority of the key guidelines for using capitation. In short, capitation works best when:

- it compensates for high-frequency, low-cost services;
- those services are clearly defined as part of the contract;
- the number of members is statistically significant;
- the provider can control the utilization of services for which he or she is assuming risk; and
- members are educated on accessing providers.

This last point must not be underestimated. Where capitation fails, one contributing factor will likely be that members were not adequately educated by the plan.

Following the above guidelines, however, is not enough. In order to successfully transition from an environment accustomed to FFS medicine to an environment that functions well under fixed payment, several straightforward but often violated guidelines should be followed. Markers of a successful transition to capitation payment include that the system:

- Be responsibly introduced and expanded when reasonable. The capitating payer has an enlightened self-interest to see that provider organizations "walk before they can run." Plans that pass on or providers that accept capitation without a transition court disaster. Such a transition at best includes a limited and defined period under which the provider is either paid a capitated amount but then guaranteed a minimum FFS equivalent, or paid on an FFS basis but then provided with a calculation of how he or she would have performed under capitation.
- Covers services that a majority of physicians would be expected to provide. Not all physician offices provide the same mix of services, and neither payer nor provider should expect that all provided services will be capitated.
- Includes payment adjustments to reflect expected demographic variations. The most effective adjustments to payment are based on self-reported health status by the members themselves.
- Derives from a clear, underlying relative value scale for pricing units of service and is based on specific volume assumptions.

- Compensates PCPS directly for assuming the responsibility for managing the overall care of their panel and for bearing financial risk. Primary care capitation should derive from more than a simple calculation of unit use multiplied by unit cost. To be fair it should include a consideration for the PCP's role as case manager.

Capitating Specialists?

In recent years some cogent arguments have been made against capitating PCPS and in favor of capitating specialists. Critics of PCP capitation have argued the following points (Berenson 1997).

Primary care services represent a small percentage of total healthcare expense. Under traditional FFS medicine this may have been as little as 10 percent of the healthcare premium. Even under gatekeeper models it rarely accrues to much more than 12 or 14 percent of the premium. Specialists, on the other hand, would minimally be expected to account for twice that amount and perhaps as much as three times.

Capping PCPS encourages referrals to specialists. This argument holds particularly true when PCPS are capped for their services only and not for all physician services, a model that seems unlikely to succeed. The argument, however, holds less water when PCPS are capped for all office-based physician services including those of specialists.

The definition—and perhaps even the role—of primary care can be disputed. Since the more widespread adoption of primary care–based delivery systems, some physicians, most notably obstetricians and gynecologists, have argued that they provide primary care services. This argument legitimately underscores a weakness in defining primary care by specialty. Actually, however, it may not be the definition of primary that is in question, but the practice of using specialties to define it. Primary care, defined by function and the types of services, can be reasonably and properly identified.

FFS encourages PCPS to handle more. As demonstrated earlier, FFS reimbursement encourages utilization. This argument applies most suitably to preventive services or those services that can be more cost effectively provided by the family practice or internal medicine physician than the medical subspecialist.

Specialists would revert to consulting role. If paid under FFS, PCPS would arguably have more incentive to see the patient and only refer to the specialist when required. However, specialists can counter in some notable instances that overall cost effectiveness and quality are improved in the long run by immediate and direct access to a specialist for specific conditions.

A recent study sponsored by the U.S. Agency for Healthcare Research and Quality and conducted by RAND researchers suggests that these specialists may be right, or at least not wrong (Kapur et al. 2000). The study compared expenditures for physician services in both closed and open (point-of-service) model HMOs in the Midwest covering 50,000 working-age enrollees. Interestingly, the gatekeeper model experienced unadjusted expenditures that were 27 percent higher for PCPS, 25 percent higher for specialists, and 26 percent higher for total overall costs. While a regression analysis did indicate that enrollees in the gatekeeper model were more likely to be female, older, and have more chronic conditions, the study concluded that even adjusted for these considerations, expenses in the point-of-service option were lower as the result of higher utilization levels in the gatekeeper model.

All of these arguments seem to carry some weight and logic; yet none seems unassailably convincing or compelling. Moreover, even if we were to find the logic or appeal of capitating specialists to be irresistible, we should not underestimate the practicalities of doing so. At least three come to mind.

First, if we wish to follow already established guidelines (consistent with statistical significance principles), we will only capitate those with a higher volume of fairly routine, low-cost procedures. While this might include the hospital-based services such as radiology, anesthesia, and pathology, these specialists will be quick to point out that they cannot control utilization.

Second, selecting or designating a single specialty group can be technically difficult unless the funds flow through the PCP. We have seen this "pod" concept work well. Asking members to select a specialist upon enrollment, however, has not proven a common practice.

Third, selecting a specialty group must be worth the political and technical effort. Less-than-well-integrated provider organizations, and particularly PHOS that are cosponsored by hospitals, will find the task of exclusively selecting a specialty group from among several to be well outside their political will. And regardless of who designates the capitated group, offering the patient only a single specialty selection may not be convenient, practical, or desirable.

In fact, the number of capitated contracts held by specialty groups nationally more than doubled from 1999 to 2000. We will not venture a guess as to whether that trend will or should continue. However, we will conclude that the various arguments for capitating specialists simply underscore that financial payment mechanisms, like structures, are tools, each with its own advantages and inextricable disadvantages. Each must be considered in the context of the overall health plan design and philosophy. At the least we must conclude that capitating specialists is no more a silver bullet than is the use of capitation for any physicians.

SUCCESSFUL RISK-BASED CONTRACTING: CRITICAL ELEMENTS

Risk-based contracts can work. Payers and providers in various, albeit limited, parts of the country have made and continue to enjoy successful risk-sharing arrangements up to and including capitation. That they do not work universally allows us to reasonably infer that the fault lies in ourselves and our application of the tool, not the tool itself, in some combination of the plan, the provider, or both.

Where provider organizations successfully manage dollars within fixed-payment risk-based arrangements, we can point to multiple elements that prove critical to success. Easily summarized and seemingly self-evident, realizing these prerequisites is nevertheless no easy matter. Moreover, as the provider organization moves from less to more financial risk, each consideration takes on more importance.

For capitation, for instance, each is mandatory. For that reason we will address each requirement in terms of a capitated arrangement.

Experienced and Willed Staff

A fundamental requisite, particularly for capitation to succeed, is the presence of an experienced and qualified management and support staff. The increased economic risk and financial accountability requires a quantum leap in the organization's ability to manage scarce dollars and focus its resources and patient care processes. While staff with a traditional or exclusive experience in hospital management may be capable of understanding the technical aspects of capitation, organizations that recruit staff from the "payer side" with a thorough, more intuitive understanding of the implications of those technical considerations and a will to make the necessary changes succeed best.

Adequate Revenue

The capitation level must be adequate for and appropriate to the level of risk assumed. The PMPM amount should be justified by detailed actuarial and utilization data on the population for which economic risk is being assumed or a similar population. This means that if a payer is using rating methodologies that increase premium based on expected higher costs for a specific population, provider payment should be similarly and correspondingly increased.

Physician Leadership

Administrative staff cannot typically take the lead in advocating to or even communicating with the majority of participating physicians. Rather the administrator's job is to engage physician leaders who can. Those leaders must be knowledgeable, committed, and involved in the management of the organization and the allocation of resources to patient care and administrative functions.

Medical Excellence

The willingness to assume risk presumes a certain level of quality waste—realized or not—within the healthcare delivery system. It further presumes that only the provider organization will be characterized by the excellence of its medical management program to advance quality initiatives capable of reducing cost. The use of care management strategies (e.g., clinical pathways, guidelines, and case management algorithms) will pervade the organization that succeeds under capitation.

Information Systems

Discussed at length in chapter 6, fundamental to successful capitation is the information system's capacity to identify the physicians, encounters, and resource costs associated with the care of a specific patient and in the aggregate for defined populations or particular health problems. The risk-bearing provider organization must be able to provide decision support to clinicians engaged in real-time patient care while also producing reports that are of use in managing (1) the organization and its various products, (2) specific categories of service, and (3) the cost and use patterns associated with specific diseases and attributable to specific physicians. (Chapter 6 describes this three-tiered reporting structure.)

Putting Specialists at Risk

The best performing managed care organizations evolve toward sharing risk with specialists, who direct the majority of resource utilization. Such risk sharing can be in the form of global payments for inpatient procedures, capitation, or even risk pools. Whatever the form, sharing risk with specialists creates a symmetry of economic interests between the physicians.

If specialists are not at risk, PCPS should be at partial or full risk for specialty services. Although some large HMOs still capitate PCPS for their services only and retain the risk for specialty costs and utilization, we cannot imagine a more illogical approach. Such an arrangement discourages primary care utilization while encouraging specialty referrals—exactly the opposite of what is desired.

A Tangible Risk-Reward Relationship

Well-designed mechanisms for sharing risk and reward between the involved parties must accompany the development of any level of risk-based contract. Too often, for instance, hospitals do not do as well as they might under DRGs because of lack of physician support. This, combined with the need to put specialists at risk for less-than-optimal resource utilization, is precisely why we argue for the use of global contracting (i.e., case payments inclusive of both physician and hospital services) in lieu of DRGs. Typically the reward level should parallel the degree of risk being assumed by the different parties and their varying ability to control specific components of risk. For example, to encourage efficiency in inpatient care, a typical arrangement might offer physicians a 50-50 share with the hospital in any surpluses in the hospital inpatient care (referral) risk pool.

Control over the Service

Finally, the successfully capitated provider organization will be very specific in excluding from the capitation agreement those patient care services that are not under its control. Consider the example of transplantation services in the case of a small- or medium-sized community hospital, which may lack both reasonable contractual access to those services and the scale of covered lives to spread the economic risk associated with such high-tech tertiary care.[3] For the same reasons the provider organization assuming capitated risk will implement stop-loss and reinsurance provisions to protect itself against exceptionally high-cost and uncontrollable cases.

No single formula for success exists in risk-based contracting. Nevertheless, these elements will come together in some form or combination to reflect the kinds of attributes discussed in detail in this book (see chapter 6).

CONSIDERING CAPITATION QUALITATIVELY

The financial implications aside, when the topic of capitation comes up many providers argue that it "compromises quality" by providing an incentive to "withhold care" and is therefore unethical. Yet does capitation really compromise quality? Is it really inherently unethical? And can we truly set financial implications completely or definitively aside in the first place? As Kin Hubbarb used to say on the radio, "When a fellow says 'It ain't the money, it's the principle of the thing,' you kin bet it's the money!"

Dr. Donald Berwick, who led the National Demonstration Project on Quality Improvement in Healthcare in 1990, definitively considered the relationship between quality improvement and capitation, examining the relationship between quality improvement and payment mechanisms (Berwick 1996). We have seen little if anything that adds to or detracts from this series in the interim, particularly with regard to Berwick's central premise.

Berwick suggests that the link between quality and capitation relies "on the system of care in which it is used and on the competence and willingness of the doctors and the delivery system to improve their own work." In other words, this link is what we might summarize as the "culture of quality" or "context of care" into which the payment mechanism is placed. Will capitation result in withholding care in some clinical environments? We would not be surprised. Does it do so necessarily and by definition? Probably not. In fact, in the context of a culture committed to quality improvement and steered by standards of excellence, "capitation can encourage better decisions and facilitate the productive redesign of systems for the delivery of care" (Berwick 1996). Rather than necessarily compromise care, fixed payments of whatever type can be used to create a "rational financial contest that vastly increases the opportunities . . . to make changes that result in better and more efficient care for patients and communities" (Berwick 1996).

There is no question that payers have used capitation in numerous instances, whether wittingly or not, to inappropriately shift risk to providers for issues outside of their control, and no doubt providers have been hurt as a result. However, as discussed throughout this chapter, providers contracting at risk have a responsibility to understand the sources and nature of risk as well as to implement the infrastructure necessary to manage it if they accept it. Moreover, risk-based payment mechanisms, particularly when inappropriately designed, can clearly create incentives for PCPs to "dump up" to specialists and for any capitated physician to make more money by doing less. But how is that more or less ethical than FFS payment that provides the strongest possible incentives for doing more as well as the motive and means to do so in deeply discounted markets? Is it not as likely that FFS payment encourages duplicate, marginally effective, or inappropriate services, exactly as we see in the study of Wennberg and Gettelsohn (1977)?

IS CAPITATION WANING?

Although widely reported of late, it would appear that news of capitation's demise may be somewhat exaggerated. On the contrary, at least three national studies suggest that capitation continues to be heavily used in markets across the country and is even expanding under certain conditions.

According to the 2000 Capitation Survey[4] the overall number of capitated contracts held by independent provider associations (IPA) and multispecialty groups declined in 2000 for the third consecutive year and for the second consecutive year for those held by PCPs, while the number of capitated specialist contracts more than doubled from 1999 to 2000. For these provider organizations the percentage of the total revenues that derives from capitation is down as well. However, capitation still "represents nearly half of the total revenues for primary care groups and PHOS and roughly one-third for multi-specialty and specialty groups" (National Health Information 2000a). Even more to the point, total revenues from capitated contracts continued to grow for all types of provider organizations, including hospitals, with the exception of multispecialty groups.

According to a report that tracks IPA payment typed by the number of revenue sources IPAS continue to rely heavily on capitation revenue. For IPAS with two sources of revenue more than 56 percent is derived from capitated managed care contracts; for IPAS with three sources of revenue that figure climbs to 79.33 percent before dropping as IPAS add a fourth and fifth source (Lareau 2000).

The recently published *Third Annual Evergreen Re Managed Care Indicator* (Evergreen Re 2000) reports that the number of provider organizations involved in capitation increased by 10 percent over a prior study to approximately 66 percent in the past year.

Not everyone agrees on the future of capitation either in terms of what it may or should hold (Deloitte & Touche 1999). However deceptively simply its equation is, capitation itself, its role in financing and delivering healthcare, and the relative sophistication of both payer and provider organizations, not to mention their relationships, all combine to present too complex a scenario for simplistic appraisals such as "good," "bad," "effective," or "antiquality." That very complexity may conspire to work against capitation as the most extreme form of risk sharing.

However, given the evolving challenges of managing healthcare's emerging sources of inflation, we do not anticipate that capitation will disappear as one of the primary means of risk-based contracting; rather, we expect the following.

- *Providers and payers will be more selective.* Those in the game are learning what it takes to manage risk and who has what it takes to do so.
- *Risk will be adjusted.* As discussed earlier, simply using age and sex adjustments probably does not adequately compensate for potential variations in resource utilization based on the enrolled population. Payers will employ, and providers will require, adjustments that better predict the demands of a specific population on the delivery system. Such adjustments would most

effectively consider the self-reported health status of the enrolled population.

- *Capitation payments will become flexible.* Critics of capitation can reasonably argue that even a properly adjusted fixed capitation payment provides not just an incentive to provide only appropriate care, but an incentive to withhold or deny care. Absent any adjustment for the achievement of qualitative goals and given the broad gray area that the term medical necessity creates, such criticism cannot be effectively countered.

- *Alternatives to capitation will be used.* Finally, because risk sharing makes so much sense as a means of aligning incentives between payers and providers newer payment mechanisms, such as global payments and even payments for episodes of care, will likely evolve (Emery 1999). Like everything else in healthcare, we can expect payment mechanisms to evolve.

CONCLUSION

Risk derives from numerous sources, some within and some outside the provider's control. Insurers and HMOs use various underwriting and rating methodologies to adjust for this risk and compete for business. Managed care contracts should reflect the risk levels and risk-adjustment methodologies of the local market between health plan and provider organization and between provider organization and provider.

Appropriate reinsurance can limit risk of high-cost cases. Premium (or capitation) reasonableness derives from numerous variables and cannot be judged based on the amount alone. Capitation rates include underlying assumptions about the scope of services, utilization levels, unit costs, and rating adjustments that contracting providers must understand. As a prospective payment mechanism rather than reimbursement methodology, capitation creates simultaneously positive and negative incentives; those incentives must be managed in the context of a system of care. Each organization must develop a rationale and methodology for allocating funds that makes the most sense in the context of its particular goals and objectives.

NOTES

1. We make the pointed argument here that enlightened payers will treat the at-risk provider as they would any knowledge worker who is directly employed. Aside from any legal standing to the contract and the nature of the contractual relationship, the payer should find it in their best interest to ensure that contracted providers, particularly physicians, are as satisfied with their compensation as possible, not unlike any other professional within the organization.

2. Accepting this premise requires that the provider view the negotiation of a risk-based contract as only the starting point of their managed care strategy and that the "heavy lifting" begin with the challenge of managing the quality and cost of the contracted services.

3. Interestingly, however, community hospitals in heavily capitated markets that direct but do not provide a high volume of specific specialty care services may wish to accept capitation for those services and then subcontract with a tertiary care center. Such an approach makes more sense than a myriad of community hospitals in the same market each attempting to provide, for instance, coronary artery bypass surgery.

4. *Capitation Rates and Data* (National Health Information 2000c) and *Capitation Management Report* (National Health Information 2000b) also provide useful and timely information about trends in prospectively paid healthcare.

REFERENCES

Axene, D. V. 1992. "Pricing, Risk, and Reimbursement." In *Making Managed Care Work*, edited by P. Boland. Gaithersburg, MD: Aspen Publishers.

Berenson, R. 1997. "Strange Bedfellows: Paying Fee for Service to Primary Care Physicians While Capitating Specialists." *Managed Care Week* 7 (35): 6.

Berwick, D. 1996. "Quality of Health Care. Part 5: Payment by Capitation and the Quality of Care." *New England Journal of Medicine* 335 (16):1227–31.

Birkmeyer, J. D., S. M. Sharp, S. R. Finlayson, E. S. Fisher, and J. E. Wennberg. 1998. "Variation Profiles of Common Surgical Procedures." *Surgery* 124 (5): 917–23.

Dartmouth Medical School. 1999. "Quality of Medical Care in the United

States: A Report on the Medicare Program." *The Dartmouth Atlas of Health Care 1999*. Chicago: American Hospital Association.

Deloitte & Touche. 2000. *U.S. Hospitals and the Future of Healthcare*. CITY, STATE: Deloitte & Touche.

Emery, D. (Ed.). 1999. *Global Fees for Episodes of Care: New Approaches to the Purchasing of Healthcare*. New York: McGraw-Hill.

Ernst, F. R., and A. J. Grizzle. 2001. "Drug-related Morbidity and Mortality: Updating the Cost-of-illness Model." *Journal of the American Pharmaceutical Association* 41 (2): 192–9.

Evergreen Re. 2000. *Third Annual Evergreen Re Managed Care Indicator*. 2000. [Online information; retrieved 9/17/01] www.evergreenre.com.

James, B. 1993. "Implementing Clinical Practice Guidelines Through Clinical Quality Improvement." Frontiers of Health Services Management 10 (1): 3–38.

Kapur, K., G. F. Joyce, K. A. Van Vorst, and J. J. Escarce. 2000. "Expenditures for Physician Services Under Alternative Models of Managed Care." *Medical Care Research and Review* 57 (2): 161–81.

Lareau, G. B. 2000. *National Directory of Physician Organizations, Second Edition*. Robert Jenkins.

National Health Information. 2000a. *2000 Capitation Survey*. Atlanta, GA: National Health Information.

National Health Information. 2000b. *Capitation Management Report*. Atlanta, GA: National Health Information.

National Health Information. 2000c. *Capitation Rates and Data* 5 (11).

Wennberg, J., and A. Gittelsohn. 1982. "Variations in Medical Care Among Small Areas." *Scientific American* 246 (4): 120–34.

Williamson, J. W., P. G. Goldschmidt, and I. A. Jillson. 1979. "Medical Practice Information Demonstration Project: Final Report." Office of the Assistant Secretary of Health, DHEW, Conract #282–77-0068GS. Baltimore, MD: Policy Research Inc.

ADDENDUM A

"TAKING HEALTH STATUS INTO ACCOUNT WHEN SETTING CAPITATION RATES: A COMPARISON OF RISK-ADJUSTMENT METHODS" (FOWLES ET AL. 1996).

Objective

To compare performance of different health status measures for risk-adjusting capitation rates.

Design

Cross-sectional study. Health status measures derived from one year were used to predict resources for that year and the next.

Setting

Group-network health maintenance organization in Minnesota.

Participants

Sample of 18- to 64-year-old ($n = 3,825$) and elderly (aged ≥ 65 years; $n = 1,955$) members enrolled in a network-model health maintenance organization in Minnesota.

Main Outcome Measures

Total expenditures in the year concurrent with the health status survey (July 1991 through June 1992) and total expenditures in the year following the survey (July 1992 through June 1993).

Results

Capitation adjustment based on demographic measures performed least well. Both self-reported health status measures and diagnoses predicted future expenditures twice as well as demographics. When predicting costs for groups of patients rather than individuals, the demographic model worked well for average groups but tended to overpredict healthier groups and underpredict sicker groups. Ambulatory care groups based on diagnoses performed better than self-reported health status both in the retrospective models and across healthier and sicker groups.

Conclusions

Without risk adjustment, capitation rates are likely to overpay or underpay physicians for certain patient groups. It is possible to improve prediction using health status measures for risk adjustment. When selection bias is suspected and administrative data are available, we recommend a risk-adjustment method based on diagnostic information. If diagnostic data are not available, we recommend a system based on simple self-reported measures, such as chronic conditions, rather than complex functional status measures.

REFERENCE

Fowles, J. B., J. P. Weiner, D. Knutson, E. Fowler, A. M. Tucker, and M. Ireland. 1996. "Taking Health Status into Account when Setting Capitation Rates: A Comparison of Risk-adjustment Methods." *Journal of the American Medial Association* 276 (16): 1316–21.

ADDENDUM B

FOUR APPROACHES TO LINKING INCENTIVES TO CAPITATED CONTRACTS

Why apply incentives? The following models represent the basic alternatives.

Model 1: Fixed Capitation with Withhold

- Establishes a single, common-rate PMPM adjusted for age, sex, and risk
- Single, flat amount withheld as a percentage of capitation (usually between 10 percent and 20 percent), reducing the effective FFS equivalent
- A withhold is returned based on performance of (1) individuals, (2) peers, or (3) the organization

Model 2: Fixed Capitation with Incentive Fund

- Single, adjusted PMPM
- A common fund is established as either (1) an expense line item, or (2) a percentage of net income
- Paid out on a point system quarterly or twice annually, increasing the FFS equivalent
- Payout based on performance of (1) individual, (2) group or peers, or (3) the organization

Model 3: Absolute Scale of Variable Capitation

- Establishes a payment corridor (versus a fixed amount) built around a targeted or expected cap rate
- Prospectively adjusts within corridor based on actual performance on a rolling basis (e.g., three months); adjustments are made frequently (quarterly or even monthly)

- Performance measured on a common scale that can include several categories and gives the same targets for all

Model 4: Relative Scale of Variable Capitation

- Establishes a payment corridor as above
- Prospectively adjusts payment as above
- Performance measured relative to peers tiered by quartile or quintile; must define peers
- Can be funded by savings (as a percentage) or as a reserve pool

ADDENDUM C

PARTIAL RISK CONTRACTING

Many times organizations want the benefits associated with developing programs to effectively manage risk but they do not have the financial capacity or the desire to take total risk. Organizations that find
themselves in this position should look for ways to share the risk with
the managed care organization. These risk-sharing arrangements can
take many forms.

Percent-of-premium Budget Model

This model requires that a capitation budget be developed for an
agreed-to scope of services as described in this chapter. Once the budget is developed an agreed-to percentage of premium is available to
cover the included scope of services. The provider then agrees to cover
these services for the agreed-to percentage. Should the actual cost of
providing the services exceed the percent of premium allowed, the
provider agrees to take responsibility for the first x%, with the payer
covering anything else. If the provider does better than the budget, the
provider shares the savings with the payer according to an agreed-to
formula.

   In the following example, the payer and provider agreed to a
scope of services and determined that 75 percent of premium is
an appropriate amount to cover these services. They further agreed
that the payer will be responsible for the actual costs of providing
these services that exceed 82 percent of the premium. Should actual costs be less than 75 percent of the premium, the payer and
provider agreed to share the savings on a 50-50 basis. At the end
of the year it was determined that the actual expenses were 78 percent
of premium. Because the provider accepted the risk up to 82 percent
of the premium, the provider must cover the 3 percent difference
in costs.

Capitation-based Model

Some payers want providers to accept capitation and the providers do not have the infrastructure or experience to accept risk. As discussed in chapter 6 providers should not accept capitation unless they have the necessary infrastructure to manage risk. If the market is such that the providers feel compelled to enter into a capitation arrangement without the necessary infrastructure, the provider should seek to limit their risk. One way of doing so is to use risk corridors tied to specific utilization patterns as in the example of capitation given in chapter 2.

Percent of Prior Years' Experience: Direct Contracting

Some markets contain employers willing to contract directly with providers or provider organizations. In these markets an approach for the provider organization wanting to take risk might be to take a percentage of the actual average medical expenses experienced over past years. The provider then agrees to deliver the scope of services for that percentage. In addition, in order to limit their risk the provider agrees to accept the risk for a certain amount in excess of the average. The employer will then cover anything in excess of this amount as in the following example.

An employer approaches a PHO and indicates its willingness to contract exclusively with the PHO for its employees' health benefits. It has had the same benefit offering for the last five years. The average annual expenses to provide these benefits have been $1 million, with last year being an average year. They are facing a 10 percent increase in premium this year and would be willing to direct contract for the $1 million it spent last year. You have reviewed this with your actuarial consultant and believe that you can manage for this amount; however, you want to minimize your exposure. You propose that you will be responsible for the first $1,100,000 and that all costs in excess of this amount will be shared equally with the employer.

CHAPTER 5

Negotiation of Effective Contracts

"Not everything that counts can be counted, and not everything that can be counted counts."

—*sign hanging over Albert Einstein's office at Princeton*

INTRODUCTION: This chapter is designed to provide an overview of the negotiating process. In addition, comments on contract terms and other helpful tips will be presented. The chapter is not intended as a complete guide to negotiation.

Managed care contracting may be approached from two vantage points. The first is that of the typical buyer-seller relationship in which the hospital, physician group, or other healthcare organization is the provider or seller of services and the managed care plan is the buyer of services. The second approach is the emerging model of providers locking into long-term partnering relationships with managed care plans in which together they share risk, sell services, and share the profits and losses of the venture. In many markets there are a variety of health plans, not all of which will survive. Thus, it is important to determine which plans will be the surviving health plans and lock in long-term relationships with them.

The information in this chapter should not be construed as legal advice. Use this information to guide you in your managed care contract negotiation. Please consult an attorney before executing a managed care contract.

NEGOTIATION

Negotiation is the process whereby each party strives to enrich not only itself but also the other party to create a mutually beneficial relationship. In the negotiating process there are often several levels of negotiation going on during each mediation. For example, negotiators might be trying to achieve organizational objectives (e.g., locking in a long-term contract, maximizing payment rate) or personal objectives (e.g., pleasing the boss, getting an annual bonus).

No matter the agenda, the negotiator should be aware that the parties with whom he or she is negotiating usually do not have final authority to conclude the transaction, despite what they may assert. Negotiators are frequently presenting proposals within the limits of their authority. Thus, your role is to present enough information to the other side to educate them on your position so they can sell the ultimate deal to their superiors.

Keep personalities out of the negotiation process. Approaching negotiation from an educational viewpoint often keeps personal conflicts from entering the process. The reaction of the opposing negotiator is likely the result of constraints put on them by their organization. Educate the negotiator on your position so they in turn can educate their organization.

The Sources of Power

A major factor influencing the organization's approach to the negotiation is its use and perception of power. Power is often perceived, with each party having more power than they realize. The goal for the negotiator is to focus on the limitations to the other side's power rather than the limitations to his or her own power. Each party obtains its power from several sources.

Competition

Both sides must realize competition is always present. Even when an organization has a monopoly position competitors can often be introduced into the market. Competition then becomes a source of power to the organization desiring to introduce it.

Consistency

Acting in a consistent manner is a significant source of power. The fact that Saturn Corporation never negotiates its auto pricing, for example, is a significant source of power for that company. Having a managed care pricing strategy and consistently applying it can be an equally significant source of power to the organization.

- The health plan that pays all physicians according to one fee schedule with no exceptions is like the Saturn Corporation. Physicians know the ground rules before they open discussions with the plan.
- Health plans that have a definite approach to hospital pricing and are willing not to enter into contracts with those who want to deviate have a significant source of power.
- Health systems that own multiple hospitals in a given market and consistently require health plans to contract with all of the system's hospitals if they contract with any gain a significant source of power.
- The hospital or physician organization that has a true competitive advantage in the market can get higher prices than the competition as long as it consistently applies its pricing strategy and does not disadvantage any major payer in the process.

Information

Information is power. Each party needs to take the time to know the other party's business as well as they know their own business. Taking the time to understand such factors as definition of terms, medical underwriting techniques, product pricing, market positioning, and decision-making processes can provide valuable insight. For example, knowing how the party with whom you are negotiating is compensated and what their incentives are can be a source of power.

Personal Relationship

The development of a personal relationship between the parties is critical. Relationships help gather information and develop trust and respect among the parties. People are much more willing to work out an agreement where a relationship exists.

It is important to develop an ongoing relationship before sitting down to negotiate a contract. Once the negotiation process begins each party's motivation becomes suspect, even to those parties intent on creating a win-win relationship. If trust has been established early in the relationship, it is easier to arrive at a mutually beneficial relationship.

To ensure continuity of the relationship in the event that one person leaves the organization, it is recommended that at least two people be assigned the responsibility of developing an ongoing relationship with two key people in the top four or five health plans in the market whether or not a contract currently exists with these health plans. At least once a quarter meet with the other party in a casual, social situation if possible. Determine their expectations of the organization and monitor on a regular basis to determine whether the organization is meeting their expectations. The time to learn this information is not at the negotiating table, or worse, when the other organization decides to terminate the relationship.

Treat the other party as customers or potential customers. Hospital organizations routinely survey their patients, physicians, and even their personnel to determine their satisfaction levels with their organization. These same hospitals rarely survey payer organizations. Surveying the payers is just as important because if their needs are not being met, there may be no patients to survey. The hospital organization that routinely determines the needs of the health plan and meets those needs will be better positioned as a payer-friendly organization than the competition.

Developing personal relationships helps the negotiator determine the personal needs of the other party. These needs are just as important to meet in a negotiation; however, rarely are they as obvious as the organizational objectives. For example, maybe the other party has just had an unsuccessful negotiation and now wants to prove himself, or maybe she is looking for another position and is not interested in the long-term effect a contract will have. This kind of information is rarely learned over the negotiating table, but can prove very valuable in developing a negotiating strategy.

Preparation

Successful negotiation begins with thorough preparation. Take the time necessary to get to know the buyer and the buyer's needs. Review the public information that is available. Health plans have to file quarterly information reports to the state insurance commissioner, and hospitals have to file cost reports. Thoroughly review this information.

It is not possible to use good negotiation tactics without a good negotiation strategy. During the preparation phase develop the strategy including what tactics you will use and when and how you will use them.

THE NEGOTIATING FRAMEWORK

The framework for negotiations is as important as the ultimate content of the contract. Setting an appropriate stage for the discussion of contract objectives and terms considerably enhances the prospect of a win-win relationship. Thus, the outline of the structural framework for risk-based contract negotiation is presented. All of the steps in the outline apply to the provider organization, whereas only selected steps relate to the health plan.

Step One: Determine Your Long-range and Strategic Objectives for Negotiation

Possible objectives for a hospital or provider organization include the following.

- Increase or diversify the population served by the provider organization. This might mean targeting specific services or specific population centers (e.g., the more affluent suburbs) for growth.
- Maintain market share of patient volume in light of increased competition.
- Position the organization to attract highly qualified physicians.
- Stabilize the revenue base of the organization by replacing variable (fee for service–based) revenues with a more certain income stream (e.g., capitation).
- Develop long-term contracts with the major health plans in the market area.

Possible objectives for a health plan include the following.

- Increase market share of covered lives (in general or specific markets or products) in the face of increased competition.
- Improve the profitability of the health plan.
- Develop new product offerings to remain competitive.
- Shift the risk for certain products (e.g., Medicare and Medicaid) to the provider organization.
- Meet corporate objectives (for national companies).
- Increase control over the outpatient and pharmacy costs being experienced by the health plan.

Step Two: Determine the Negotiating Team and the Spokesperson

It is recommended that a team of individuals be involved in the negotiation process for both the health plan and the provider organization. The team strategy has several advantages, including:

- better buy-in to the ultimate outcome of the negotiation by the organization;
- increased ability to listen and hear the other side's needs and views;
- decreased likelihood of making a mistake;

- better understanding of the issues because more experts are present;
- increased ability to delegate and divide the work so it can be done in a more timely and thorough manner;
- better continuity should there be turnover within the organization; and
- an opportunity to train future negotiators.

The major disadvantage of using teams is that significantly more coordination is required among team members. This often lengthens the negotiation process.

The mix of talent, interpersonal skills, and expertise on the team is critical. In addition, the level of organizational leadership represented on the team sends an important signal to the other party regarding the significance attached to the particular negotiations.

Not all team members need attend each negotiation session. However, they should be involved in setting the objectives, negotiating strategy, and negotiating parameters when specific questions arise involving their area of expertise and when there is the need to modify the negotiation strategy.

Team members will vary depending on the size and complexity of the organization. For example, in a rural hospital the team might just consist of the chief financial officer (CFO), business office manager, and a managed care consultant. For a large provider organization, the team might consist of the vice president of managed care, director of information services, CFO, and director of medical management. Health plans should include those individuals responsible for information services, claims systems, finance, accounting (where capitation and percent-of-premium contracts are involved), medical underwriting, and medical management as well as the contracting staff.

An organization must also realize when it does not have the appropriate expertise and employ outside consulting help as necessary. This is particularly true for organizations embarking on risk-based contracting. The use of a consulting actuary is critical to avoid the pitfalls that often present themselves in such arrangements.

Once the team is in place it is important to select a spokesperson. This individual will direct the negotiations for the team. Other members of the team should not speak during the negotiation session unless directed to by the spokesperson. This is perhaps the most difficult aspect of teams for the team members themselves. All are bright, talented people in their areas of expertise and have a desire to contribute. However, they must be willing to subject themselves to the use of a spokesperson in order to ensure that one view is presented, it is consistent, and there is team agreement in the approach. To do otherwise weakens the team.

Step Three: The Initial Meeting

The initial meeting should be structured for the provider organization to accomplish three things.

1. Obtain whatever information you can regarding the plan. (The questions cited in Addendum A provide a guide to important areas to probe.) In addition, the provider should obtain whatever information is available in the public domain regarding the payer. Reports required to be filed with the state insurance commissioner are a valuable source of information.
2. Determine the objectives of the health plan.
3. Request critical information necessary to submit a proposal according to the desired parameters required by the plan and the provider organization. The provider organization must remember that it is the seller of services and must structure its response to meet the requirements of the plan, the buyer of services.

The health plan's goals for this initial meeting will be to outline its needs and expectations of the provider organization and determine if there are any particular issues the plan needs to be aware of and address.

The provider organization must complete a number of practical steps prior to developing a formal proposal to the health plan.

1. In most cases it will be easier to use the plan's contract as a starting point. Obtain a sample contract from the plan and compare it with your contract checklist (see the Appendix at the end of the book for an example) to determine what issues exist. This will help the provider organization identify any issues that must be addressed in its proposal. The contract should be given to appropriate legal counsel to identify any substantive legal issues. This should assist with the development of the negotiating strategy. Remember that the ultimate business deal itself is the responsibility of the provider organization, not the attorney. When selecting an attorney to assist in your contract negotiations, choose one who will listen to your objectives and help fashion a proposal to meet the organization's business needs while pointing out legal risks.

2. Determine the potential effect on the organization's appeal to patients and physicians. Will the image of the health plan cause a loss of physician support or market share? The health plan has already made an assessment of the provider organization's effect on its growth potential within the market.

3. Determine if there is sufficient time for the organization to implement the systems changes required to contract effectively with this health plan.

4. Review any political considerations involving the organization's physicians, physician-hospital organization (PHO), or board. For example, what if a contract already exists between the PHO and the health plan and the health plan decides that it wants to contract individually with the physicians and hospital? If the payer is currently paying below-Medicare rates for their HMO product, will your physicians accept this? Do you have exclusive contracts with your hospital-based physicians and if so, will the proposed rates be acceptable to them? Will additional physicians need to be added to the medical staff? Does the plan require special treatment or priority status for services rendered?

5. Review the likely response from other payers to the organization contracting with this particular health plan. Will they view the

contract as a major threat to their market share plans and erode the relationship with the provider organization?

6. Determine whether you will be permitted to participate in all products of the plan or just in specific products.

Many plans have formalized the process of obtaining information from provider organizations through the use of requests for proposals. This offers a systematic opportunity for the health plan and the provider organization to establish clearly the key terms of the contract for both parties and the criteria on which the proposed contractual arrangements will be judged.

A concern for provider organizations is the health plan that takes an organization's proposal and shops around with other provider organizations to get them to match the proposal. Then the health plan does not contract with the provider organizations or it negotiates to further reduce the original proposal. Although this practice is unethical, it has been done by some unscrupulous health plans. In order to prevent such a situation from occurring, provider organizations will enter into an exclusive period of negotiation with the health plan. Each party agrees to negotiate in good faith and use their best efforts to conclude the negotiation within the agreed-to timeframe. The signing of this agreement raises the level of commitment each party is making to the other.

Step Four: Determine the Organization's Bottom Line

Upon receipt and evaluation of the information requested from the health plan, the provider organization's management should determine its financial and qualitative objectives for the contract. The idea is to determine your goals but not fix your position in the negotiation. Having established its bottom-line objectives for the financial and qualitative outcomes of the contract, the organization can be more precise in balancing price, market share, and other contract terms.

The Appendix at the end of the book is a managed care checklist that includes the major terms in managed care contracts and a offers framework for evaluating these terms. It would serve those negotiating contracts well to develop their own checklist to address the important issues for their organization. This type of tool ensures that important terms are not forgotten. Remember that the nonprice terms can be as important—or more important—than the price terms (see below).

The health plan must also determine its bottom line consistent with its overall marketing and pricing strategies. For national managed care companies, corporate constraints on contract terms must also be reviewed.

Step Five: Determine the Organization's Negotiating Strategy

The next element of the negotiating framework is to determine the organization's negotiating strategy. It is best to set high expectations that are justified based on your objectives and that can be supported with data (the other party's data when available). Those who set high and reasonable targets and stick to them often get what they want out of a contract. Be the first to suggest major terms rather than reacting to others' suggestions. Negotiation has a tendency to play on personal aspirations, as in the following example.

An HMO comes to a healthcare organization requesting a per-diem proposal. The organization knows it can provide the service for a minimum of $800 per day but would like to get at least $1,200 per day. When the health plan submits its desired pricing first and puts $600 on the table, the natural reaction is that the healthcare organization will immediately begin to move its expectations toward the lower end.

In essence, the negotiator begins to negotiate with him or herself, assuming the health plan will never accept the higher proposal. If, however, the provider organization proposes the higher amount first, the targets tend to move toward the higher amount. Although initially counterintuitive, placing your offer on the table first will achieve results closer to the desired outcome than will waiting and responding to someone else's offer. Setting your expectations high should obviate the fear of "leaving something on the table."

A corollary to this is never to accept the first offer—even if the offer is acceptable to the organization—because both parties need to feel that the results are a win-win relationship. If one party accepts the other's initial offer, most often the feeling by the party making the offer is that something was left on the table. In long-term relationships, maintaining the relationship is as important as the final deal. In order for each party to be satisfied with the ultimate arrangement, it is important never to accept the first offer.

To be successful in your negotiations you must first be willing to set high and reasonable targets, stick with them, and make the first proposal. Remember that you will never know whether your proposal will be accepted if you do not ask. Do not worry that something might be left on the table. Be satisfied with the targets that are set.

Once the strategy and targets are set, write them down. It is interesting to note how many times a negotiation breaks down after the parties have both achieved their initial goals but one suddenly wants to achieve more. By writing down the strategy and targets everyone in the organization can buy in and those charged with the negotiations can proceed to achieving a win-win agreement.

Finally, in developing the negotiating strategy, follow the 80/20 rule: 80 percent of the time should be spent on the 20 percent of the issues that are really significant. The development of an agenda to guide each negotiation session will help keep the negotiations focused in this direction.

Step Six: Develop a Specific Proposal

The next step is the development of the specific proposal. Many times the managed care plan will request pricing in a form that the health-care organization does not believe is in its best interest to manage (e.g., per diem, capitation). If the healthcare organization does not bid using the form requested and does not receive the contract, it should not be upset. If that is the way the health plan wants to buy it, that is the way the healthcare organization has to sell it. Provide alternatives to the original request, but bid as designated by the buyer while protecting the organization from the risks assumed.

Take the time to analyze the available data to fully understand the risks being assumed. This means familiarizing yourself with all of the

nuances associated with the proposed contract and pricing arrangement, including obtaining assistance from outside experts as necessary. Then structure your proposal so that the organization is paid for
those risks.

Before finalizing the proposal, determine if it passes the "keep it
simple" test. You have to administer what you negotiate; therefore,
simplicity should be valued. Once the proposal is final, obtain review by legal counsel and other parties within the organization who
might be affected by the agreement. Then present the proposal to the
health plan.

Step Seven: Identify Areas of Agreement and Disagreement

When negotiating the proposal both parties should explicitly identify
areas of agreement and disagreement. The points of agreement serve
as the key stepping stones to overcome or at least mitigate areas of
disagreement. They provide a clue to the other party's underlying
objectives, allowing both the provider organization and the health plan
to explicate what they wish to achieve through the contract.

Documentation is very important throughout the negotiation process. Minutes should be kept of each negotiating session. Confirm in
writing to the other party those items on which there is basic agreement as well as those issues that are still outstanding. This documentation can prove invaluable should one or more of the parties involved
in the actual negotiation leave their respective organizations. How the
agreement was arrived at and the intent of the parties is easier to determine if minutes of the negotiating sessions are available.

Step Eight: Resolve Areas of Disagreement

Having identified the areas of agreement and a more complete understanding of the parties, the next steps are to (1) determine on which
issues to concede, where not to concede, and where to postpone further negotiations; and (2) present alternatives that meet both parties'
objectives and reconcile the areas of disagreement. Here it is important to determine the underlying objective to be met and fashion a

proposal to meet it. For example, many health plans do not want to contract using sliding scales because the plans want to know their costs today as they are pricing their product today. One way to address this concern is to enter into a long-term contract and fix the first year's rate based on the plan's forecasted volume. The second year rates are determined based on the actual volume received in the first year. The hospital is only at risk for not receiving the volume it expected in the first year, and the health plan accomplishes its objective of knowing its prices in advance and not experiencing retroactive adjustments.

Step Nine: Execute the Contract

After finalizing the contract it is recommended that the parties have periodic, ongoing meetings to make sure that both are meeting the other's needs and expectations.

NONPRICE TERMS WORTH NOTING

As previously mentioned, nonprice terms can be as important as the price terms. Below are some specific nonprice terms worth considering.

Definitions

Definitions constitute perhaps the most boring section of a contract, but they are also the most important. Take the time to read and understand the definitions in a contract. Remember that a lawyer's responsibility is to protect you from liability, not to protect you from a bad business decision. It is the negotiator's responsibility to take the time to ensure that the business deal makes sense.

Products Covered

It is important to understand which products are included in the contract. Does the contract apply to indemnity products the insurer may manage? Does it apply to workers' compensation products? Are discount clubs able to access the network? Will the network be leased to others? Will the provider be required to participate in all products offered by the plan? These important issues must be clearly defined.

Favored Nations

Favored nations is a provision requiring the provider to give the payer its best price. In the event that the provider gives a better rate to another managed care plan, the provider is also required to give it to the managed care plan with the contract containing the favored-nations provision. Two considerations are worth noting regarding favored-nations clauses.

First, the determination of when to apply such a provision is simple when all of an organization's contracts are under the same basic payment structure (i.e., all are per diem, all are discount off of charges). However, how do you compare prices when all of the contracts are based on different pricing schemes (i.e., some discount off of charges, some per diem, some diagnosis-related groups)? For example, to determine a comparable per diem rate, do you convert a case rate to a per diem by dividing the case rate by the average length of stay of the managed care plan who has the favored-nations provision, or by the length of stay of the managed care plan who has the case rate? Is it fair to compare different pricing structures when each has its own unique incentives and different degrees of risk? Unless these questions are addressed when the contract is being negotiated and a clear agreement is reached, potential conflict may arise over these issues in the future.

Second, for those who negotiate physician fees, favored nations may be a valuable contract term to include. Most health plans that pay on a fee-for-service basis use the resource-based relative value system that Medicare uses. Most health plans use one fee schedule per product for all physicians. This is the perfect situation in which to ask for the favored-nations provision that the health plan will pay you their best rate for a physician in your specialty. If they are unwilling to include this provision in the contract, the physician needs to probe further to ensure that he or she is getting the best rate.

Benefit Design

If the benefit design is important to you because it is the major channeling mechanism for getting patients, it should be an attachment to the agreement. For example, if you are told that the benefit design on a preferred provider organization (PPO) product requires that those patients going out of network will have to pay 36 percent coinsurance—and this is important to you because you believe this will deliver the patients to your hospital—it needs to be in the agreement. Omitting it permits the PPO to change the benefit design while maintaining the rates that you have given.

Another important contract provision is a requirement that the health plan enforce its benefit designs. Consider the example of an out-of-network provider who waives the coinsurance requirement for the patient. This is insurance fraud. However, to avoid being accused of fraud the out-of-network provider notifies the health plan in writing that it routinely waives coinsurance. Now the situation no longer constitutes fraud because the element of deceit is not present; the insurance company knows that the coinsurance is being waived. If the coinsurance requirement was a key method of channeling business in return for the discount, that point is lost unless the insurance company agrees to enforce its benefit designs and require its members to pay the higher coinsurance.

Network Design

Usually when a hospital is seeking a contract it first determines which hospitals will be in the network and then prices the contract accordingly. The premise is that if the major competitors are not going to be in the network, the hospital should gain volume. Thus, the hospital can offer the discounts necessary to get the contract. The difficulty is in how to structure the arrangement and not run afoul of the antitrust laws while getting the volume or benefits from the contract that was negotiated. Three suggestions are offered for consideration.

First, indicate in the contract that the initial network that resulted in the terms given consists of hospitals A, B, and C. If at any time during the term of the contract the managed care plan wants to change its network, it must give the hospital a predetermined number of days of advance notice and an opportunity to renegotiate the rate. If the hospital is unable to negotiate a new rate it may terminate the agreement.

Second, create a geographic area defined by zip codes and permit the managed care plan to contract with facilities within the area that add up to a predetermined number of licensed beds as listed in a specific edition of the *AHA Hospital Guide*. The facility's entire count of licensed beds is used for every contract the managed care plan has. This gives the managed care plan the option of changing hospitals without getting the hospital's approval, but limits the number of licensed beds contracted within a given area.

Third, develop different fee schedules for each combination of hospitals that are of concern and make this an attachment to the contract. The managed care plan has the freedom to contract with whomever it wants in the market—it just has to pay the prenegotiated price.

Coordination of Benefits

A coordination-of-benefits provision applies when the health plan is the secondary insurer. The following example will help clarify the issue.

A patient incurs a hospital bill of $10,000. The patient's primary insurance covers 80 percent of the bill, and her secondary insurance is responsible for 20 percent. If the secondary insurer has a contract with the hospital that would have paid the hospital $6,000 had they been primary, under the standard coordination-of-benefits language the secondary carrier will pay the hospital nothing. The patient is no longer liable for the 20 percent and the hospital receives no payment.

This is how standard coordination-of-benefits language works because it was originally written for billed-charge arrangements. With all of today's special arrangements, the application is different. The managed care plan may make the argument that it is responsible for giving the patient the incentive to use the specific hospital; if the patient did not have the managed care plan's coverage—even as the secondary payer—the patient would not have used this hospital. This is a valid argument when the hospital has an exclusive or near-exclusive arrangement with the plan. The less exclusive the arrangement, the less valid the argument. Consider the following two approaches for dealing with this issue.

1. Rewrite the coordination-of-benefits language so that it pays the hospital up to billed charges but does not require the plan to pay the hospital in excess of the contracted rate. If this approach is pursued, be aware that most health plans are ill equipped to manage such an arrangement and the hospital will need to carefully monitor each occurrence to ensure that proper payment is made. Most plans will not agree to this approach because they cannot administer the provision.
2. Recognize what is being given up by permitting this provision and consider it in the totality of the negotiation.

Clean Claim

Attempting to define clean claim has created many problems for billing offices. Two approaches are suggested.

1. Develop an attachment that clearly defines the elements required for submission for a claim to be considered clean.
2. Use the following language: "A claim will be deemed to be clean if within xx days from the date of receipt, no written notice to the contrary is received by the provider."

Penalty for Late Payment

The most common penalty for failure by a payer to pay a clean claim within an agreed-to period is for no discount to apply. If a penalty is included in the contract, it is important that a method exist at both the plan and provider levels to administer the penalty; otherwise it would be better to negotiate favorable terms elsewhere that can be administered.

New Technology or Services

Contracts, particularly long-term ones, need a provision to deal with new services and technology. Most contracts contain a requirement that all services offered by the hospital be included in the contract; thus, a hospital must provide these new services to the plan's members once they begin to offer them to others. Two approaches are suggested.

1. When a new service or technology is made available, a small committee made up of three persons from the hospital and three persons from the plan will review and recommend the appropriate pricing arrangement. This will be done within a predetermined number of days from the time the managed care plan receives notice. If a recommendation is not forthcoming within the agreed-upon timeframe, the CEOs of both the hospital and plan have a predetermined number of days to arrive at an agreement. If they are unable to arrive at a mutually agreeable rate, the issue is submitted to binding arbitration. It is important to establish and enforce timelines for each step.
2. The hospital will give the plan 90 days advance notice prior to implementing a new service or technology. The plan and hospital will negotiate an appropriate pricing arrangement during the 90-day period. If they cannot arrive at a mutually acceptable arrangement, the hospital is not obligated to provide this service to plan members. If it provides the service to plan members, it can bill and collect from the patient.

Termination

It is recommended that contracts other than discount-off-of-charge contracts terminate on a specific date and not automatically renew. It is too easy to forget the automatic renewal and be locked into an extended term. Further, the annual review of each contract gives you a chance to see if the contract is meeting your expectations and propose modifications if necessary.

Leased Networks

If the contract is with a PPO that leases its network to many payers, it is important to retain the ability to terminate an individual payer. When an individual payer is not meeting the contract obligations the provider should have the right to notify the PPO and give the PPO an opportunity to work with the payer to correct the issue. If the payer continues to breach the agreement, the provider should have the right to terminate that specific payer without having to terminate the entire contract.

Unilateral Right to Amend the Contract

Neither party should have the unilateral right to amend the contract. Notice and an opportunity to terminate if not satisfied with the proposed change is a necessary requirement in all contracts. This should also apply to material changes to operations manuals or other documents referenced in the contract to which the parties agree to comply.

New Products

The introduction of a new product should require a contract amendment. For example, if a hospital has a contract with an HMO and that HMO decides to introduce a point-of-service (POS) option, it is important that the contract require an amendment for such a product offering. Without such a requirement the hospital could find that it is part of a POS offering at HMO pricing without HMO incentives to use the network.

Audit Function

Providers should implement an internal audit system to audit the high-cost claims as well as a random sample of routine claims. Health plans want to pay claims correctly. They do not deliberately try to pay claims incorrectly; however, mistakes occur. If payment arrangements that cannot be processed automatically are negotiated, they will require manual intervention. These manual interventions often lead to interpreting the contract, which leads to mistakes.

The best approach for both the provider and the payer to reduce payment errors is to negotiate arrangements that can be processed electronically and automatically. Even when this is done mistakes can be made when loading the information into the computer system and when making changes to the system. Therefore, it is in the provider's best interest to audit claims payments.

Consider, for example, that a large hospital may employ three full-time persons to audit all claims. Their results consistently show a recovery in excess of $3 million annually in net underpayments to the hospital. The investment in these three positions more than pays for itself.

CONCLUSION

The contracting process is an evolving one. The issues present today may be resolved through legislation (e.g., prompt pay) or common contracting approaches. New issues will continue to emerge. The key to successful contracting is developing and maintaining strong relationships with the crucial payers in your market. These relationships will assist you in resolving those contract administration issues that will arise over the course of the contract term in a manner that benefits all parties.

ADDENDUM A

DETAILED PLAN ANALYSIS

The following are some critical questions to ask a managed care plan to ensure that you have a clear understanding of their organization and objectives.

Control

- What is the ownership structure of the organization?
- If part of a large national company: What does the local operation control? Network? Product design? New product development? Product pricing? Payment arrangements?
- Would they contract with the organization's PHO?

Marketing

- Who are the target physicians?
  - What approach will be used to sign up the physicians?
  - What involvement can the hospital have in this effort?
  - Are specific groups being asked to participate?
  - What are the criteria for physician selection?
  - Is the plan closed to any category of physicians?
- Target market
  - What size employer groups will be targeted?
  - What type of employer groups will be targeted?
  - Will Medicare or Medicaid be included?
  - Is this a major market or a secondary market for the plan?
- Target hospitals
  - What criteria are used for hospital selection?
  - What is the proposed network?
  - Are there restrictive covenants or guarantees regarding network?

- Marketing plan and products
  - What type of products are being offered? For which products does the local plan have bottom-line accountability?
  - Will the network be leased to other payers? Silent PPO? Discount clubs?
  - What are the enrollment projections for each product being offered?
  - Are some products just offered to national buyers and others offered locally?
  - What are the demographic characteristics of the expected enrollment?
- Benefit designs
  - For each product what is the proposed benefit design? Are members or enrollees encouraged to use certain in-network providers over others?
  - Will the plan commit to enforce the benefit designs with its members?
  - Do they know of any providers in the market that might be waiving coinsurance to attract out-of-network members? Do they have any systems in place to monitor their out-of-network usage and investigate if usage is higher than expected?
- Information to be provided to hospital during contract
  - Will they provide the number of enrollees using in-network versus out-of-network providers?
  - What are the membership data?
  - Are payers under contract (updated at least every 90 days)?

Financial

- Physician reimbursement
  - How are physicians reimbursed by product?
  - What will be the rate of payment compared with current Medicare resource-based relative value system rates? How does this compare to the competition?

- Will they provide a favored-nations provision for the physicians by specialty?
- Are there any incentive plans being employed to encourage use of one facility over another?
- Hospital reimbursement
  - What payment method is requested?
  - What flexibility do their information systems have with respect to payment methods used?
  - Are other methods being used in other parts of the country?
  - Is there an incentive program for the hospital if certain objectives are met? Would they consider such a program?
- Coordination of benefits
  - How is this handled?
- Premium
  - What are their premium targets? How do these compare with others in the market?
  - What are their utilization assumptions in days per 1,000 enrollees?
  - What percentage of the premium is allocated to administration and profit?
  - What is their medical loss ratio for each risk product?
- Confidentiality
  - How do they assure the confidentiality of rate information? Are total charges and plan responsibility on the explanation of benefits?

Medical Management

- How is their medical management program structured by product?
- Do they use on-site nurses?
- What are their expectations regarding using hospital personnel to assist them?
- Does the plan have the authority to retroactively deny claims?
- What are the policies affecting the physicians?
- What are the appeal rights?

- What is their ratio of percentage of denied days to total days?
- If a patient day is denied, is payment also denied to the physician?
- Who is responsible for precertification? Hospital? Physician? Patient?
- Are specialty services limited to specific providers (e.g., MRI, lab)
- Do the contracts with providers contain indemnification language?

Administrative

- Claims processing
  - How are claims processed? All in one location or many different locations?
  - Does the hospital receive timely notice of receipt of claims or claims that are not clean?
  - How flexible can the local management be regarding contract arrangements?
  - Does the plan have its own claims system or does it lease time from a shared system?
  - What percentage of clean claims are paid within 15 days of receipt? Thirty days?
  - If there is an agreed-to penalty for late payment, does the information system automatically adjudicate it or is a manual process required?
  - Do the local staff have the authority to handle claims issues or do they just refer them to another office?
- How many personnel are in the local office? Types and responsibilities?

CHAPTER 6

Infrastructure Necessary for Success in a Risk Environment

"As provider-at-risk payment strategies become increasingly dominant, they will force healthcare providers to replace old strategies that measured and managed revenues with new strategies that measure and manage cost. Quality improvement theory provides a set of tools to do exactly that—to understand, measure and manage healthcare delivery processes and their associated costs."

—*Brent James, M.D., Executive Director, Institute for Health Care Delivery Research*

INTRODUCTION: Chapter 3 argues that managed care's significance derives from how it establishes buyers and sellers of healthcare. Chapter 4 proposes that the sharing of risk between buyers and sellers can create aligned incentives. This chapter follows up on both notions with an overview of the infrastructure components necessary to be successful in a risk environment.

We discuss the attributes of successful systems, setting the stage to examine the functions that allow the realization of those attributes. Establishing a solid, comprehensive approach to maximizing physician participation, devising physician payment mechanisms, and credentialing is essential, as is setting performance standards that can inspire and direct the participants. Finally, establishing a systematic approach to that measuring and analyzing performance must include a consideration of sources of data and information systems.

IMPLICATIONS OF RISK-BASED CONTRACTS

We reiterate that sharing risk can not only align incentives between health plans and providers, but risk-based contracts can actually enhance the provider organization's ability to pursue its very mission —assuming that mission concerns itself with providing the "highest quality healthcare at the lowest possible cost." How? By creating incentives to measure and manage costs rather than measure and manage revenues.

Tactical Implications

Figure 6.1 illustrates the reversed requirements for profitability under fixed (eg., risk-based) versus variable (eg., fee-for-service) revenue conditions. Briefly summarized, this graphically represents how, under fee-for-service compensation, charges are a source of revenue, whereas fixed compensation charges are a source of costs. This graphic sets the stage for considering, throughout the remainder of this chapter, the management tools and techniques required for profitability under these new conditions of belief and experience.

Operational Requirements

When a health plan shifts risk to a provider organization, it will typically shift responsibility for a variety of administrative and medical management operations, and the provider organization will ordinarily want to assume this control. While these responsibilities will vary from plan to plan, market to market, and even time to time, they can be extensive. In addition to contractual responsibilities to actually deliver care, assumption of risk may include associated or derivative responsibilities for:

- claims payment and adjudication for contractually committed services, even those not directly provided by the provider organization;
- HMO-specific administration, including defining terms and reporting measures as the HMO may generically or uniquely define them;
- reinsurance, or providing stop-loss coverage for services provided under the terms of the contract;

Figure 6.1: Tactical Implications of Managing Costs vs. Revenues

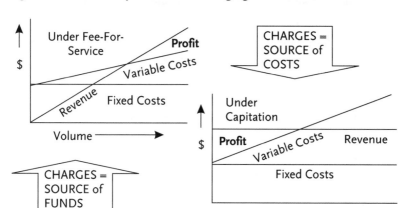

- certification of lab sites or other ancillary diagnostic services with which the provider organization contracts;
- arranging for, credentialing, and providing healthcare services, which may include contracting with nonmember providers, ensuring access within certain time criteria, and credentialing;
- notifying the health plan of out-of-plan and out-of-area admissions or services (for which the payer may or may not be responsible according to the contract);
- precertification or referral authorization with response requirements with regard to any services for which the health plan may have retained some or all of the risk;
- preventive care according to whatever language and standards may be included in the contract;
- rehabilitation, skilled nursing facility, or other services per HMO-specific criteria, using (as the contract stipulates) specific providers or networks for various services;
- advising the health plan of differences in anticipated versus actual length of stay;
- reporting changes in provider hours, addresses, open status, etc. with regard to specific criteria that the health plan may require as part of the contract;

Infrastructure Necessary for Success in a Risk Environment 185

- member services, which can include requirements to maintain a 24-hour answering service, written member orientations, complaint documentation, and an appeals process; and
- other health plan–specific responsibilities with regard to various administrative or delivery system activities such as formulary or pharmacy benefits management programs or member education.

While no two plans will share exactly the same set of responsibilities and few are likely to pass all of the above responsibilities to a provider organization, health plans have shifted administrative and delivery system responsibilities to provider organizations for those services for which they have assumed financial risk.

Implications

Consider the example of a large HMO that capitates physician (or physician-hospital) organizations for physician and outpatient services only. It retains risk for all hospital services, including mental health and chemical dependency, and skilled nursing, pharmacy, and outpatient surgery services. For services for which it passes risk to providers, it also passes along the administrative responsibility for managing that risk. The practical or operational implications of these responsibilities mean that, for instance, accepting responsibility for claims payment and adjudication implies that the provider organization must acquire and manage the information systems and staff capable of paying and subrogating claims, coordinating benefits, managing multiple payment methods and calculations, maintaining multiple fee schedules, producing explanations of payment and benefits, creating sophisticated reports for the contracted health plan, managing the provider organization itself, and managing the contracted members or providers. Moreover, each subsequent responsibility implies the need to competently execute the numerous other administrative functions associated with member services, medical management, and so on.

Following are the five overarching implications of this type of contract for the provider organization.

Competence Means Everything

Note that many of these functions parallel those of a health plan itself; even some of the largest and most able plans in the country still struggle with these functions to provide a high level of service at low cost. Competence in these managed care skills will determine the level of effectiveness and efficiency and thus the degree of success in the marketplace. Yet the effective and efficient administration of these responsibilities will not likely be achieved through the skill sets that are effective at managing hospitals or health systems. Health systems that have succeeded in achieving a level of competence in these areas have, for the most part, looked outside their organizations for the required management expertise. Additionally, such plans will likely aggregate a significant number of at-risk enrollees. Justifying the resource to build the infrastructure inevitably means significant economies of scale. In contract administration size is important.

Ownership Means Nothing

To paraphrase Drucker's observation (1995), the independent practice association (IPA), physician-hospital organization (PHO), integrated delivery network, or other structure employed by providers may matter dearly to the physicians, hospital, and health system, but in the marketplace its very existence is irrelevant. What will matter to the health plan, its enrollees, and its employer customers in the market is the ability to create added value through the excellent execution of its assumed responsibilities. Even the organization's physician members and sponsors will quickly lose interest and withdraw support if claims are not paid on time and its office staff cannot verify eligibility or answer questions quickly and accurately. Performance, not ownership, counts.

Extensive Collaboration Required

If it is to be done well, shifting, or particularly sharing, risk between a health plan and a provider organization requires careful collaboration.

In effect, as we argue in chapter 3, the managed care contract itself represents a vertical integration strategy for both plan and provider. The most casual of relationships require some collaboration, and the intensity and seriousness of risk-based contracts require significant collaboration. Minimally we suggest that each organization designate various contacts who can coordinate the resolution of day-to-day questions and operational issues. Additionally, the respective organizations should meet at least twice annually, and probably quarterly, to assess progress toward mutual goals and on common interests.

Fewer and Longer-Term Contracts

Throughout this book we argue for longer-term contracts between payers and providers. For nonrisk contracts, multiyear terms may be neither required nor desired. However, to achieve the effective degree of vertical integration required by the mutually established interests long-term relationships are essential. Three-year contracts seem minimally justified for setting up the kind of infrastructure required. Five-year contracts would probably serve the parties even better. Just as significantly, because each contract will include operationally substantial requirements specific to that health plan, it is advisable to limit the number of risk-based contracts the provider organization enters into. Because such advice probably contradicts provider organizations' near-universal, if downplayed, purpose—to protect or aggregate market share—we will elaborate on this important point.

Although size is important, economies of scale simply do not aggregate across multiple contracts. In other words, the provider organization cannot realistically expect to provide administrative services for 100,000 members through ten contracts as inexpensively or effectively as it can through one or two. Each contract will contain different definitions, benefit levels and terms, covered services, and so on. In effect, each contract will therefore require the focus and concentration that a single HMO administrator would accord it. While the provider organization may succeed at providing what the market will demand for a specific contract, each additional contract will make it incrementally more difficult to excel, particularly in the face of low overall enrollment. While many provider organizations expect to lower costs through additional contracts, in reality most realize increased costs.

Hospital-based PHOs in parts of the United States have entered into as many as a dozen or more risk-based contracts with an overall average enrollment as low as a few hundred enrollees per contract. Because some contracts can include several dozen different benefit levels, the administrative permutations expand into the hundreds. This strategy thus inevitably increases costs in multiples, and administrative costs in such PHOs easily accrue to obviously unsustainable levels as high as 35 to 50 percent of revenue.

Changed Business Definition

As significant as the above implications of risk-based contracts are, we will point to one, in particular, as the most far reaching. Once the provider organization assumes financial risk for the services it provides, it assumes the same financial incentives, marketplace expectations, and fundamental business definition as the managed care organization, be it an HMO, insured preferred provider organization (PPO), or insurer. In effect, the provider organization transforms itself into a managed care organization.

Given the financial, organizational, and operational implications above, we therefore turn our attention to what makes for a successful managed care organization.

ATTRIBUTES OF SUCCESSFUL MANAGED CARE ORGANIZATIONS

Successful managed care organizations capable of bringing added value to their customers—without respect to ownership, as we have seen—will exhibit at least seven attributes. (Adapted from a list of attributes originally published by the Governance Committee of The Grand Alliance in 1993, we have substituted several attributes with our own observations as managed care theory and practice has evolved in the interim). Some of these attributes will be particularly difficult for providers to exhibit. Others appear to prove more difficult for traditional insurers. All must be addressed, each with some threshold level of success, for the managed care organization to thrive. Failure in any one attribute will likely mean failure overall.

Strategic Focus

In any industry leaders have a well-defined, market-based purpose. They articulate well-understood, widely communicated goals that respond first and foremost to customer need. While this seems self-evident, the number of both providers and insurers who fail to understand that managed care represents a fundamentally new industry with its own set of principles and conditions of belief and experience is remarkable.

Health plans with a successful history of sponsoring indemnity insurance products often narrowly view managed care in terms of the risk it represents. They instinctively seek first to avoid risk through various underwriting and rating tactics and then to shift it to providers without much thought as to the implications for either themselves or providers. Other ways in which they fail to act on new conditions of belief and experience include:

- Neglecting to put into place—or even recognize the significant role of—demand, large case, disease, and other resource management techniques and approaches.
- Using deep discounting to control physician expenses. In emphasizing unit costs over resource management (only really an option on the inpatient side), plans neglect to anticipate the resultant surge in office-based procedures, patients seen per day, and new procedures being offered by physicians.
- Not developing physician relations programs that allow plans to meaningfully engage physicians in redefining care processes that allow for reduced utilization while either maintaining or improving quality.

- Shifting risk to provider organizations not adequately structured to manage it or not providing adequate information systems support.
- Pursuing growth and market share through merger and acquisition without giving adequate thought to integrating the complex infrastructure underlying the respective books of business or contracts.

While many of those insurers who had the hardest time shifting from an indemnity to managed care mindset have either sold to or been absorbed by other plans, few health plans employ and effectively compete on the kind of principles that successful service and even manufacturing organizations in other segments of our economy employ, a systems approach to managing quality and cost, statistical quality control, and aligned financial incentives. Consider how organizations like John Deere, Motorola, Olympus Camera, Nordstrom, and others have used quality improvement, and then ask yourself how many health plans have taken a similar approach.

Getting through the proverbial "eye of the needle" presents challenges for the delivery side as well. In our experience, too many provider-sponsored organizations or integrated delivery networks came together to make the new rules drive the old system. Unable or unwilling to rethink their marketing mix—and possibly even consider redefining the business they are in—they instead calculate how many members they need to maintain their current infrastructure, how many primary care physicians (PCP) it will take to fill unused beds with patients. Such tactics seem premised on managed care as a threat to the health system rather than an opportunity.

Despite the predominance of managed care plans based on the old conditions and beliefs of indemnity insurance, managed care can actually enable the mission and purpose of the community hospital or health system; managed care can bring a strategic focus. Figure 6.2 suggests just such an approach. Specifically, this model proposes:

- a core strategic focus based on the near-universal commitment of community providers to quality[1];

Figure 6.2: Information Systems for the Market-Driven Organization

- a marketing and communications plan that differentiates and simultaneously targets two different target markets: healthcare purchasers and healthcare consumers;
- a "push-and-pull" strategy, recognizing that a strong awareness and preference on the part of consumers is needed to pull business, and an equally strong appeal to health plans, self-funded employers, and other purchasers is necessary to push business; and
- different measures of value for each of these two target markets. While certain, somewhat different measures of clinical processes and outcomes will appeal to both, other measures will be primarily of interest to one or the other.

Such a twofold strategy will apply to nearly all provider organizations in all markets. Indeed, we derive it from looking at various leaders in various markets. But what of the provider system that wants to sponsor its own managed care initiative? Can a health system successfully sponsor a health plan as part of its strategic focus? Unquestionably. Many excellent examples exist and are by no means limited to any particular geographic location. However, sponsorship of a health plan by a provider requires an unusual willingness to allow the plan to pursue its own strategic focus. Few provider organizations have seemed willing to do this.

Functional Integration

Departments and departmentalization seem to define and create the culture of the hospital: silos of activity through which we organize and arrange, budget and staff for, measure, and manage work. But as Dr. Brent James (1993) articulates so well, in the "at-risk, cost-based environment the natural unit of analysis and management is a process, not a department."

Managed care organizations must measure and manage processes and the outcomes of those processes. To be sure they need to take care of organizational basics such as budgeting for claims processors and setting targets for sales, but they recognize, as does James, that independently these areas cannot make the organization succeed. Departments can only cause the organization to fail. In this respect we can very reasonably apply Frederick Herzberg's (1966) term "hygiene factors," as opposed to "success factors." Poorly addressed hygiene factors will bring the organization down, but they cannot make the organization succeed, no matter how excellently implemented. As an entire body of quality-improvement literature from Deming to James points out, success relies on making certain that the interface between departments, facilities, and even organizations—whomever is involved in a process—goes well.

Functional integration does not require that the managed care organization own all the "means of production." To the contrary, as pointed out in chapter 3, the very fact that a contract exists between providers and payers means that both are making a decision to buy rather than make the services provided by the other. However, such integration does require the following factors.

Mutual Interests

If the managed care contract, particularly one through which the provider shares risk with the insurer, represents a vertical integration strategy for payer and provider, both must recognize that each needs the other to thrive and each should have the other's success in mind. Particularly in a risk-based contract, but certainly in any volume-significant contract, the provider has a stake in the payer's premium and the payer has a vested interest in the satisfaction, effectiveness, and even efficiency of the provider for the provider's sake. The well-managed health plan will demonstrate as much sensitivity to the physician's office and its satisfaction as the auto manufacturer will to the dealer. Again, health plans should view providers as frontline retailers, and providers should think of the health plan as their channels of distribution.

Joint Operations and Clinical Teams

The practical implication of the mutual interests described above is that providers and health plans will want to work closely with their preferred partners. The health-plan-as-public-enemy-number-one perspective must give way to regular—at least quarterly—meetings on medical management, customer services and satisfaction, and various administrative functions. Success for both parties in sponsoring mature managed care initiatives will depend directly on the other.

Difficult Distinctions

Commonly physicians and other providers concern themselves with the plan's administrative costs and see the higher medical expense ratio as the preferred allocation of resources. Health plans, on the other hand, too often seek to reduce the medical loss ratio by addressing unit cost alone. Yet to adequately realize the mission of the managed care organization—achieving clinically appropriate care in the most appropriate setting—neither perspective can prevail. The kinds of necessary systems-based tools, from software for provider profiling to developing the necessary disease-management and case-management care maps, require an investment in dollars that cannot be easily categorized as either just administrative or clinical.

Primary-specialty Care Balance

Managed care literature, historically lower premium levels of HMOs compared to other models, personal management experience in both for-profit and nonprofit managed care organizations, and straw polls taken by the authors over the last seven years all rather convincingly reinforce the role of the PCP in managed care.[2] The fact, for instance, that the HMO has continued to maintain a cost advantage over PPO and indemnity models can in large part be attributed to the role and use of the PCP in the HMO. Rather than attempt to make a case for the gatekeeper model, however, we will simply, but more broadly, advocate for both a changing role for primary care and a changing mix of PCPS to specialists.

As depicted in Table 6.1, the at-risk provider-sponsored managed care organization should optimally include approximately the same number of PCPS as specialists and consulting physicians. While we have certainly seen IPAS and PHOS perform reasonably well in managing utilization if the ratio of PCPS to specialists drops to one to two, ratios much below this should be expected to result in compromised performance. When we query seminar participants who indicate that they sponsor an IPA or PHO that is not working, a common, indeed nearly universal, response is that specialists dominate these structures.

Unfortunately for hospital-sponsored managed care initiatives, this need for primary care involvement usually presents a significant problem: the dominance of specialists on staff and throughout the medical staff structure. We can think of several reasons why specialists traditionally and uniformly play a dominant role in the hospital. They have a history of predominant use of hospitals for the services they provide. Medical staff bylaws and quality assurance programs usually organize around medical specialties, and as size allows, subspecialties, so that medical executive committees are specialty heavy. Finally, the overall—generally significantly—higher incomes of specialists allow more time away from the practice. However, it is no surprise that the structures most successful at accepting and managing risk in both Southern California and other parts of the country are IPAS rather than PHOS. Moreover, in a recent (unpublished) survey conducted by a local physician-accounting firm in Chicago, risk-bearing IPAS on average compensated their physicians 15 percent higher than risk-bearing PHOS. The 1998 survey of 24 PHOS and 22 IPAS reflected an

Table 6.1: Provider-sponsored Organization Physician Composition

Ratio of PCPs Projected to Specialists Performance

1:1	Optimal
1:2	Acceptable
1:3	Marginal
1:4	Unacceptable

average payment of 100 percent of Medicare's regional resource-based relative value system levels for PHOs and 115 percent for IPAs. Perhaps more significantly, the best-performing PHO paid its physicians 115 percent of the resource-based relative value system levels, whereas the best-performing IPA compensated its physicians at 158 percent.

We strongly advise hospitals and health systems that intend to partner with or otherwise engage physicians in managed care initiatives to do so outside the traditional medical staff bylaws.

Geographic Coverage

The American consumer's desire for convenience is well-recognized, representing one dimension of consumer-defined quality. That means convenient geographic access. Because the plan will need to provide convenient access to consumers or lose enrollment to those that do, proactive providers will realize that health plans need to optimize their geographic access. Minimally, in a small to mid-size community this will mean access on a community-wide basis. In a mid-size to larger urban environment surrounded by a significant suburban belt this will mean access on a more regional basis. In either event, the hospital or health system will want to make certain its front-line retailers— its primary care practitioners combined with outpatient and outreach programs—are geographically dispersed.

For providers content to rely on indemnity-based health plans and network PPOs as their channels of distribution, geographic coverage may not represent one of the most critical success factors. For those, however, who sponsor their own network PPOs, and particularly for those contracting on an at-risk basis, geographic access can mean everything.

Shared Risk

Contrary to what we seemed convinced of just a few years ago, capitation does not represent the sine qua non of managed care contracting. But before we completely reverse that position perhaps we should give ourselves some credit. Probably we would have been correct to suggest that shared risk, rather than shifted risk, represents the future. Having made the case for risk-based contracting in chapter 5, we will not repeat ourselves. Suffice it to say that providers expecting to succeed as managed care matures should probably not suppose that discounted fee-for-service payments will provide them with the net income to do so, unless they can command consumer loyalty or they operate in undersupplied markets.

As discussed throughout this book, contracting providers and payers must look to enlightened mutual self-interest to achieve a level of functional integration in the market.

Known, Low Costs

Minimally, health systems will want to be able to simultaneously monitor and model resource consumption from at least three different cost dimensions:

1. episode of care or diagnosis-related group, reinforcing a service or product-line approach to management (and even pricing);
2. variable costs directly attributable to specific physicians; and
3. contribution margins for their various contracts.

Health plans as well as at-risk providers will similarly want to be able to view their resource consumption along multiple perspectives, including:

- disease (e.g., asthma, diabetes, otitis media);
- provider or provider organization; and
- product or market (e.g., small group versus large group).

Specific reporting and profiling approaches will be outlined and recommended throughout the remainder of this chapter.

Information Systems

Managed care organizations seeking to position themselves on quality will add value in the marketplace by employing both push and pull marketing strategies (see Figure 6.2). Use of these well-respected tools borrowed from other industries requires that provider-sponsored entities display an adeptness at measuring and managing those outcomes important to payers and patients in five areas.

Clinical Outcomes and Processes

From cesarean section and nosocomial infection rates to medication errors and use of beta blockers after initial heart attacks, such measures will be of interest to both the payer or employer and the patient or member.

Improving Efficiencies

Managing and measuring both clinical and administrative efficiency will be critical both for internally managing quality and externally demonstrating it. From electronic interfaces and data exchange to interactive telephony, information systems will both represent and result in enhanced efficiencies.

Communications with Payers

Providers accepting risk will be required to document efficiency and effectiveness for payers. Payers who intelligently and responsibly share risk will require measures of performance from providers.

Ultimately it is their insurance or HMO license on the line with the respective state.

Communications with Members

From the basic requirements to produce member education specific to an enrolled population to allowing members to enroll online and even register for and schedule office visits and procedures, member communications is critical to a quality organization; information technology is in turn critical to member communications.

Service and Accessibility

Almost indistinguishable now from member communications because of technology, member service begins with a panel of informed and service-oriented providers for whom outcomes can be increasingly documented and continues with the ability to provide immediate—perhaps even online—answers to questions about claims or benefits.

The corresponding demands on information systems for providers at risk essentially require that providers provide a matrix of information systems, considered later in this chapter.

Subjective Barriers to Provider-sponsored Organizations

Whether the provider organization intends to sponsor an HMO, PPO, or even a subsidiary organization such as an IPA or PHO, at least three subjective barriers exist. Subjective barriers cannot be measured, quantified, or otherwise documented. Nevertheless, and perhaps consequently, they may present the biggest challenges to success.

Lack of Discipline or Purpose

A managed care organization must add value in the market without regard to ownership. The sponsoring organization will only be successful to the extent that it is willing to do whatever is required to meet the customer's needs, not its own.

Engaging Physicians

Managed care strategies test physician–health system relations. Physicians may challenge a proactive strategy, particularly with regard to risk assumption. The physician leadership or commitment required, particularly with regard to time constraints, may be absent. In fee-for-service–dominated markets physician fragmentation may prevent integrated approaches such as disease management.

Employer Perception

Employers may be skeptical of providers' interest in managing care and more inclined to trust in externally imposed solutions to utilization management.

FOUR PRINCIPLES

Few if any managed care organizations today, whether sponsored by insurers or providers, fully exhibit all four of the principles that world-class competitors in other industries do; in the past the economic and marketing environment did not require them to, but they will need to in the future.

Principle One: Approach Managed Care as a System

We probably cannot with any level of integrity apply the dictionary definition of a system to healthcare in the United States. Although we regularly, if euphemistically, refer to "the U.S. healthcare system," as Dr. John Wennberg (1977) put it, "The American healthcare system is no system at all. It is a random hodge-podge . . . What [medical care] you get depends on where you live—not what disease you have." Wennberg's studies concluded that the capacity of a city or region determines demand.

Nevertheless, with the growth and maturation of managed care, a systems perspective seems to be slowly emerging. Like the first leaves of spring, almost a decade ago the National Demonstration on Quality Improvement in Healthcare gave evidence of the need and validity of looking at the multidimensional relationship between healthcare quality and healthcare cost across departments and functions, not simply within them. And we are beginning to examine outcomes across providers.

A systems approach in managed care means that we must manage and work together differently than we have in the past and, for the most part, do today. It requires the full-time employment of integrated approaches to case and disease management. And because the minority of members inevitably generate the vast majority of costs for services—most likely delivered by a network of specialized participants—case management requires management protocol along three dimensions. Vertically, case-management techniques are required to control quality and cost of high-cost cases. Horizontally, techniques for prevention, detection, and early intervention must be provided across the membership, particularly to those least inclined toward participation in such activities. And diagonally, health plans and the continuum of providers must find ways to integrate their activities and coordinate their own core competencies.

Of course the very best HMOs, and some health systems, have done this for some time. But it is not easy. A history of dependence on risk avoidance rather than risk management and a legacy of central control and the financial imperatives of indemnity insurance mean that traditional insurers will want to sponsor managed care products rather than evolve into managed care organizations. Network PPOs, the clearinghouse form of managed care, simply cannot put together the required infrastructure. (Even today, their philosophy of find and punish the worst rather than celebrate and reward the best rests on a philosophy antithetic to a systems approach.) Hospitals probably face even greater barriers. They actually direct only slightly more patient care services than do network PPOs, which direct none. They typically cannot put together the infrastructure, or sometimes the resolve, to engage those who do direct patient care, the physicians. Hospitals typically exhibit a psychologic legacy of risk aversion to begin with and are generally more focused on contracting for volume and market share. Finally, physicians, who otherwise seem naturally positioned to direct this organizational transformation, are ill-trained for a systems approach (at least in the case of allopathic physicians), inadequately organized and capitalized, ill-disposed to the kind of collaborative team-oriented approach that is required, or some combination of the above.

Our impediments to progress are not represented by what we do not know, but rather by what we think we know or by conditions of belief and experience that are no longer valid.

Principle Two: Manage Cost Through Quality

Predicated upon a systems approach, managed care organizations will recognize that the quality-cost relationship is a complex one. The perspective, so dominant among physicians (particularly specialists), that any attempt at cost control necessarily compromises quality simply does not hold up in healthcare any more than it does in other industries. Simply admonishing against cost cutting is at best the equivalent of warning that sailing too far west will spill you over the end of a flat world; at worst it speaks to a self-interest incongruent with the history and ethics of medicine itself. Rather, a systems approach to healthcare mandated by integrating financing and delivery creates strong incentives to improve quality while addressing costs; these mandates will shift the paradigm from the services so dominant in our society to prevention, primary care, and least intensive intervention.

Principle Three: Employ Statistical Quality Control

The tool that other industries apply to their systems to achieve quality and control cost—statistical quality control—embodies the maxim that you do not manage what you do not measure. In healthcare this adage most patently embodies itself in physician profiling, although increasing its scope includes outcomes measurement techniques and is founded on work done by Walter Shewart that dates back seven decades.

The application of provider profiling and outcomes measurement, of far-reaching consequences in managing the quality-cost relationship, actually has greater significance for and impact on the social structure of the organization. Provider profiling in particular places "knowledge" (for which we could subsequently read "power" or "control") in the hands of the worker and transforms the basic function of management. Drucker (1995) underscores this for industry, and his lesson ought not be lost on either insurers or hospitals, although it often seems to be.

Knowledge workers, simply put, know more about what they do than management does and ultimately even could. In healthcare, of course, the knowledge worker is the physician, and this approach runs counter to our history of either insurance or hospital management. It replaces the command-and-control mentality of directing or supervising work with the leadership responsibility for providing the worker with the ultimate right—and responsibility—to fulfill the function of his or her profession, ministering to the sick and helping the healthy. Truly revolutionary, in a very real sense this principle is almost Marxian, although it takes Marx to another level, for we are dealing here with data rather than dollars and knowledge, not capital, as the main means of production.

The true managed care organization must recognize the primacy of the physician as the ultimate knowledge worker and director of the overwhelming majority of resource utilization. Such an organization will not attempt to manage the physician through profiling, but will use it to empower the physician. Ultimately the various hotly debated issues and difficulties of profiling physicians (which are imposing and dealt with later) stand in the shadow of this basic issue: will profiling be used to control or empower the physician? Thus, the intent of provider profiling emerges as a central issue.

While, with reason, physicians will feel threatened by statistical quality control, in an enlightened organization based on total quality management principles physician profiling can and actually should serve to advance the scientific process on which medicine is based. Physician profiling provides the required feedback to physicians who otherwise receive little if any quantified data on their behaviors.

Principle Four: Manage Costs as Well as Revenue

Both traditional insurers and the preponderance of providers have, virtually from their inception and literally as part of their cultures, focused on managing revenues. Both passed along increasing costs to their customers, who for the most part passed it on to theirs. Immature managed care models or organizations turned their attention to partially managing costs; because this cost management is only partial it was less pursued than the systematic approach described above. They sought to reduce unit costs (e.g., physician fees or per diems) combined in some measure with strategies for cost avoidance (e.g., underwriting practices designed to avoid cost) or targeting the largest and slowest moving game in the forest, inpatient days. The results have been largely ineffective at best and counterproductive at worst. Costs have been shifted rather than reduced, physicians have increasingly been given incentive to behave in their own short-term best interests (behavior reinforced by the cottage-industry nature of private practice), and managed care has been discredited. We would be tempted to say that the proverbially low fruit is now off the tree, but in healthcare much of the fruit has actually migrated to higher branches.

Mature managed care organizations must now advance their organizational strategies to actually managing total cost, the combination of cost arising from both unit utilization and unit price. Days per thousand and lengths of stay are, under externally imposed third-party programs, about as low in many communities as they are likely to go. Hospital pricing is on something of a rebound, if anything. And across the country payers are feeling pressure from physicians who simply did not go to medical school for the kinds of incomes that managed care organizations are offering them. Yet few people genuinely believe that the fat that is marbled throughout the system—the quality waste that could be but is not being saved—has lessened. Consequently many observers, particularly those who look at managed care as simply deep-discounting strategies, think the industry has run its course precisely at a time when the challenge has never been greater.

ESTABLISHING STANDARDS

The above discussion argues that the starting point for mature managed care organizations of the future rests on setting standards of performance, both clinical and administrative (to the limited extent to which these two functions can be delineated).

The Starting Point

We could easily argue that establishing standards is the starting place for managed care organizations for any number of reasons. After all, we have discussed the relationship between quality and cost and posited that even if cost is the desired end, the pursuit of quality is the only sustainable strategy for getting there. In chapter 7 we further suggest that healthcare will increasingly be measured on such performance standards—particularly if we move to a consumer-driven model (in contrast to our current payer-driven model), whether assessing the health plan itself or the providers who comprise the panel, consumers will demand to see such performance standards. Today consumers can go to any number of web sites and see comparative data that, however imperfect, are as ubiquitous as they are inevitable. But neither of these legitimate and compelling reasons is the right reason to begin with the establishment of standards of performance.

The more experience we have gained as "managers," the more deeply we should understand that while we may be able to manage money, systems, data, or other resources, we cannot manage people. Instead, when it comes to directing organizations of people, leadership, not management, is required. And the best people want to be lead for the best reasons—reasons that appeal both to their competence and their character, both of which the experienced executive should be concerned with.

Multiple Perspectives

Nowhere is this truer than in healthcare. Healthcare workers are knowledge workers who, as we will discuss later, know more than we do about their jobs. Whether they have received an MBA or medical degree, executives cannot know more than the people doing the work. The more educated and trained these people are, such as in a healthcare or managed care organization, the more they will seek higher reasons to do the things they do. Chances are they can make a living doing what they do almost anywhere. (If not, you probably do not want to hire them.) Whether hired or contracted (as with physicians in the network-model managed care organization), knowledge workers will want to know that the organization stands for something more than cutting costs or probably even making money, that it is making a difference as a managed care organization, ensuring and expanding access and husbanding limited resources, and achieving better outcomes and enhancing people's lives.

Healthcare workers in provider-sponsored organizations will want to see measures of performance ranging from clinical outcomes and customer satisfaction to growth and perhaps even research and education. Healthcare consumers, as employees and workers, will want to see that their employers are active and creative purchasers of healthcare, providing care through managed care organizations that are well-organized, efficient, and effective. Doing so will require a quality-driven purchasing initiative that promotes the kind of total quality management and continuous quality improvement efforts that they participate in within their own industries. Such purchasing initiatives will simultaneously incorporate best practices and benchmarks to drive improving performance while promoting performance consistency across the network, something universally lacking in healthcare as documented in the Dartmouth Atlas (2000). Ultimately they will seek to determine the value of care to guide purchasing decisions for their employees using either Health Plan Employer Data and Information Set (HEDIS) measures or, as Digital Equipment Corporation did several years ago in issuing a request for proposal, going beyond HEDIS to include standards in five major categories of performance:

- administration and member services, including measures of proximity to delivery points, provider ratios, access or availability guidelines, and benchmarks for member services and assistance;

- clinical quality, including an assessment of organizational structure and philosophy, credentialing practices and performance, practitioner performance monitoring, clinical management and delivery, and confidentiality;
- behavioral health, recognizing the differences from acute medical or surgical care, measures-included benefit design, accessibility and triage, case management, outcomes measurement, continuous quality management, and prevention;
- information systems and reporting, actively evaluating the managed care organization's strategy for technology, means of data collection, reporting capabilities, enrollment and utilization protocol, and member and provider satisfaction; and
- finance and contracting, beginning with financial stability but also considering premium development and multiyear trends as well as contractual protections for both the employer and the employee or member.

Finally, it is worth noting that the federal government, through the Quality Improvement System for Managed Care (QISMC), mandated that health plans providing Medicare coverage must demonstrate improvements in the quality of care beginning in 1999 with a two-year phase-in. In addition to requiring the plan to provide a policy-making body that must oversee the quality-management initiative and, as part of that initiative, ensure provider participation, the guidelines require plans to conduct at least two quality-improvement projects per year (three if the plan also contracts for Medicaid) built around 18 major standards with scores in four domains:

1. quality assessment and performance improvement;
2. enrollee rights;
3. health services management; and
4. delegation.

Most of the QISMC measures derive initially from HEDIS, but they also make use of measures from the Consumer Assessment of Health Plans Study.

Whether in three, four, or five categories, we recommend such a multifaceted perspective for establishing performance standards to assure the managed care organization's multiple constituencies that it is taking a systematic and systemic approach to quality to control cost, enhance quality, and attract the best administrative and clinical staff.

A FUNCTIONAL MODEL

We propose a functional model of management for managed care organizations. Underlying this model are three primary premises:

1. *Four functions.* A mature managed care organization has four primary, relatively discrete functions: medical management, marketing, operations, and finance. Other functions are secondary and either supportive of a single function, such as actuarial services with finance or advertising with marketing, or supportive of all four, such as human resources, information systems, and strategic planning.

2. *Interdependence.* These four functions are interdependent. Each relies upon and affects the other area such that any action in any one of the functions is likely to have some effect on another. To the extent that the effect is not anticipated or communicated, the effect is likely to be negative. To the extent or degree that management anticipates the effect of each upon the other, it behaves systematically (as discussed earlier).

3. *Primacy of medical management and physician relations.* While each function interacts and is interdependent with all three of the others, medical management—from its underlying philosophy and basic design to its daily implementation and execution— is the sine qua non of the managed care organization. It is the managed care organization's essence and raison d'être. As such, it has the greatest effect on each of the other functions and rightly occupies the central position in the model. As a corollary of this premise, because physicians continue to provide the majority of care the effectiveness and efficiency of the medical management program will rely principally upon physician relations.

Physician Relations

We arrive at last to perhaps the most challenging and critical aspect of creating the mature and effective managed care organization: engaging physicians. By most estimates physicians direct the vast majority of healthcare in a traditional healthcare delivery system, perhaps as much as 85 or 90 percent. While with the growing use of alternative and complementary therapies being directly accessed by consumers the role may be somewhat quantitatively diminished, any system designed to finance and deliver care must come to terms with the basic question of how it will engage physicians. (This question is independent of organizational structure. Whether physicians are employed, contracted with, or simply reimbursed, the considerations of physician relations remain the same and are unaffected by the specific organizational relationship.) We should be very clear: no question or decision will more comprehensively or inevitably affect the managed care organization than its approach to physician relations. Whether aware of the choice or not, the organization will choose from two basic approaches.

Patriarchy Versus Partnership

Any organization, in deciding how to govern itself, must make a make a critical choice about how it will deal with and treat those it engages, whether by contract or employment. Will management, sitting atop the corporation and accountable to the board and stakeholders, view itself as solely and centrally responsible for the success of the organization as if it were a parent or patriarch? This mindset, often so thoroughly engrained in the organization that management itself has no idea that it embraces and represents it, is particularly well-described by Peter Block (1993): "We govern our organizations by valuing, above all else, consistency, control, and predictability."

Few organizations more pointedly embody these values than most of the health plans we have encountered. With their actuarial bias and dominating insurance cultures, most health plans and insurer-sponsored HMOs and PPOs embody this mindset of patriarchy. Yet in doing so they paradoxically create barriers to the very outcomes that would make them successful in the marketplace. Again, to use Block's (1993) words, "In a high control environment, what is personal and sacred to us is denied. Autocratic government withers the spirit. In the marketplace in which we operate now, centralized control cannot create product, guarantee quality, or serve customers."

Can you think of an industry in which the professionals who direct the majority of the service are more disenfranchised than in managed care? We genuinely cannot. The command-and-control approach of much of managed care with regard to physicians over the last two decades has done a great deal to wither the spirit. Precertification and third-party review, second guessing, depreciation of the value of physician judgment, and general attribution of selfishness—fully deserved by a few but attributed to the majority—impoverishes the role of the physician and destroys productivity. This patriarchal approach saps morale, destroys motivation, and gives incentive only to self-interest. Then, rather obtusely, it condemns the very behaviors that it encourages.

How is the managed care organization to differentiate itself in the market and establish itself as market driven except with the proactive support and involvement of the physicians? How can the managed care organization, the ultimate product of which is nearly universally delivered and controlled by the physician, "create product, guarantee quality, or serve customers" when its providers are alienated, disengaged, and angry to the point of forming unions?

In contrast to this approach, the environment in which it results, and the low level of service that it ultimately provides to the member is a governance philosophy of partnership. This philosophy, Block (1993) points out:

> carries the intention to balance power between ourselves and those around us. It brings into question the utility of maintaining consistency and control as cornerstones of management. It comes from the choice to place control close to where the work is done and not hold it as the prerogative of the middle and upper classes. It also flows from the choice to yield on consistency in how we manage,

and thus to support local units in creating policies that fit local situations.

In many instances this approach appears to run directly against the grain of several of the country's largest health plans. From purposes as pragmatic as seeking to minimize information systems program variation to purposes as philosophic as promoting a common standard of care, some of the nation's largest plans opt for the consistency and predictability that control appears to offer. For the health plan considering its philosophic premise we point to the local nature of healthcare and the difficulties of centralized decision making through time and place. For the provider organization establishing its managed care strategy we recommend closely evaluating payer philosophy on this central question of patriarchy versus partnership. The managed care organization that can create an environment that prompts the physician to say to the patient "You're in the best health plan in town" will achieve greater success in the market than any competitor. It is no accident, for instance, that over the past several years BlueCross BlueShield of Illinois consistently earned the highest rating of all health plans in Illinois among physicians while enjoying twice the market share of its nearest competitor.

Physician as Knowledge Worker

As sound as the above argument for partnering with physicians is—as difficult as that may be from either the plan or physician perspective— a dramatically practical reason for its fitness exists: the physician knows more than management about what he or she does. This is so important because of the central notion underlying all health in- surance and health plans: medical necessity.

Medical Necessity

In all of the language in all of the contracts your organization will likely enter into, no more vague and ambiguous term exists than "medical necessity." On the one hand, among all the health services provided every day across the country, certainly some significant minority of care is so immediately and medically essential that withholding or denying it will result in otherwise unavoidable death or permanent disability. On the other hand, insurers daily see bills and claims for services so medically unnecessary that their submission could be—and is of late—considered ludicrous and possibly fraudulent. In the vast and overwhelming center of these two extremes lies a murky and largely uncharted landscape where necessity can be widely and variously interpreted. Like art, medical necessity may lie in the eye of the beholder.

Dual Role of the Physician as Knowledge Worker

Simply put, the knowledge worker knows more about his or her job than the executive. If we agree with current economic thinking that knowledge, rather than capital or labor, produces wealth, the knowledge worker represents the organization's true asset. And if, as presented in chapter 3, the prerequisite for both productivity and innovation is knowledge, differentiation in the marketplace relies on the physician.

Not only do practicing front-line physicians know more about what they do than does management and not only are physicians inherently closer to the work, but they serve a uniquely dual role: they provide a minority of care and direct the majority of care. Indeed the physician in an HMO most likely, through his or her pen, directs the use of more of the corporation's resources than the majority of its administrators. Thus, the physician becomes an executive of the health plan because by virtue of knowledge, "he is responsible for a contribution that materially affects the capability of the organization to perform and obtain results" (Drucker 1966).

Financial Incentives

Because of this dual role health plans often first and exclusively turn to financial incentives to encourage the behavior they seek to reward. Whether as carrot or stick, managed care organizations have sought to use dollars to promote desired behavior. Much of the literature suggests an apparently conflicting role for financial incentives. Our experience and is that while financial incentives alone will not produce desired behavioral changes in physician practice patterns, neither will programs that overlook financial incentives.

Because physicians are both provider and director of medical resources and are subject to a variety of personal, practice, and professional standards; objectives; and pressures no single approach to addressing incentives works as well as a comprehensive approach that involves several indicators. Eisenberg (1986) details a six-part program for considering physician behavior:

1. education;
2. input;
3. written guidelines, crieria, and targets;
4. feedback;
5. financial incentives; and
6. sanctions.

To this we would add two observations. First, to be positively effective at all financial incentives must follow education, input, feedback, and written standards or guidelines. Without these first four components adequately in place, the managed care organization is likely to find that the financial incentives it does use are either not effective at all or achieve some other purpose than the intended one. With these components firmly in place, a physician relations program is likely to achieve some significant measure of success that can be significantly leveraged by the application of financial incentives.

Second, the managed care organization that properly implements the first five of these components is unlikely to need the sixth. If peer pressure, education, and communications cannot address patently unacceptable or unwarranted behavior or practice patterns, the financial incentives themselves should over time ensure that a physician who does not work with the system will not find the system's compensation to be adequate. Only in the rarest of cases should a health plan or managed care organization need to turn to sanctions; if it does, it should ultimately ask how that practitioner made it through its selection and credentialing process in the first place.

Guidelines for Sharing Financial Risk

Perhaps the first guideline we would recommend in setting up a system seeking to employ physician incentives is not to shift but rather to share risk. Shifting risk—particularly for factors not fully under the provider's control such as insurance risk—can fragment the system and create inappropriate incentives. Sharing risk, however, ensures an ongoing mutual interest.

Additional guidelines are listed in Figure 6.3. While such guidelines perhaps appear simplistic or obvious, even an informal survey of health plans or provider organizations in any given market will demonstrate that most violate at least one, if not more, of these basic suggestions.

Medical Management

Physician relations then represents the fulcrum on which medical management leverages itself. Properly placed, the fulcrum allows a great deal of work to be achieved. Improperly placed, the length of the lever will offer no significant advantage. Physicians simply cannot be forced or coerced into compliance. However, like the fulcrum, the lever itself has several sections, all of which must be used in balance and consideration of each other.

Provider Panel Management and Credentialing

Just as the health plan's attitude toward physicians is critical, so is that of the physicians collectively toward the plan. The plan that has the luxury of discipline, of constructing a panel from among physicians who are open to the discipline of a managed care model, will have an inherent advantage in the marketplace. While the plan will feel the pressure for an inclusive panel for the sake of marketing ease

Figure 6.3: Premises when Compensating Physicians for Financial Risk

Characteristic of successful managed care organizations because it reverses historic incentives (managing revenue/volume), risk-based contracting (capitation, global fees, or other) will work well, particularly in primary care, if it:

- Is responsibly introduced and, when reasonable, expanded.
- Covers services which (a majority of) the physicians would provide.
- Includes adjustments for expected demographic/risk variations.
- Derives from a fee schedule based on relative value units (RVUS).
- Compensates PCPs for functioning as case managers.

FINANCIAL INCENTIVES

Representing one component of a carefully orchestrated program, financial incentive should:

- Tie to individual performance.
- Address factors which a physician directly/substantively controls.
- Allow a period of time to alter behavior before being effected.
- Consider both qualitative and economic goals.
- Relate only to concrete, objective, and relevant measures.
- Address a limited number of measures.
- Be understood and adopted by representative physicians.
- Change as the needs of the managed care organization changes.

ADMINISTRATION

Administration of any payment mechanism should be timely, efficient, cost-effective, and accurate.

and acceptability, the more exclusive panel will more likely serve as a foundation for an effective medical management program.

In establishing the requirements for credentialing the managed care organization lays out its conditions of participation. Regardless of corporate structure participating physicians within the managed care organization should have some input into these conditions and their application on an ongoing basis, particularly with regard to recredentialing. Clustered into groups representing four specific perspectives, the typical requirements for participation are as follows.

1. *Professional requirements.* These represent organizational prerequisites for moving further along in the credentialing process. It should be clearly stated in the application that meeting such criteria does not ensure participation but only allows further consideration.
2. *Liability requirements.* These elaborate on minimum criteria for consideration, principally with regard to third-party liability insurance and experience.
3. *Practice type and quality criteria.* These practice pattern criteria actually allow the health plan to differentiate itself based on the panel it has put together; it is on these criteria that participating physicians should have the most input.
4. *Management criteria.* Strictly management criteria allow, for example, the establishment of a legitimate business need to add a practice. Indeed management, in support of a specialty or particular practice with which it works particularly well, may want to reserve the right to exclude other groups.

With regard to this last set of criteria, the effect of any "any willing provider" laws that the state in which the managed care organization is incorporated must be considered. In most states such laws, however, simply define guidelines to which such management criteria must conform and do not necessarily preclude them. Nevertheless, competent legal counsel with specific experience in this question should be retained.

Demand Management

Provider panel management acknowledges that practice patterns of physicians significantly affect medical management effectiveness.

Efficient practice patterns alone, however, will not ensure success. The attitudes and inclinations of the enrolled population greatly influence demand management. For instance, one of the reasons hospital and health workers use health services at a rate significantly above the population as a whole no doubt derives from their attitudes toward access and patterns of demand.

An effective program of demand management—from member education to benefit designs that provide financial incentives—is required for a successful managed care organization. Ordinarily responsibility for sponsoring such a plan should rest with the health plan itself, although the at-risk provider has an incentive to see such educational programs in place. Providers and health plans that share risk and have a sense of partnership should regularly appraise their joint demand-management initiatives. Providers, particularly physicians, can offer valuable input in terms of patient demands for specific drugs or procedures and are well-positioned—if they can be so engaged—to provide input into member education and demand-management programs.

Health System Performance Improvement

Discussed from the perspective of a systems approach to delivering care, the managed care organization's commitment to ongoing or continuous quality improvement is the next major component of a successful medical management function. The organization's approach to identifying opportunities to improve the management of specific diseases or acute-care episodes forms the context that will define all of its remaining medical management functions. For instance, the managed care organization that involves physicians in establishing medical management guidelines, and particularly in establishing principles for their application, will advantage itself in the marketplace in a manner that will not even be visible to competing organizations, much less understood. Yet precisely because of viewing the physician as knowledge worker the plan will position itself to optimize the benefits of a systems approach.

Medical management guidelines are a critical, perhaps keystone, component of an effective program. (Recall that one of the six criteria of an effective physician relations program is written guidelines.) The following comments seem most relevant here.

- *Make versus buy.* Several commercially available sets of medical guidelines and protocols exist. The managed care organization would do well to adopt, and perhaps adapt as necessary, one of these rather than reinvent the wheel. Our preference is for those guidelines built around the notion of evidence-based medicine as having the most validity and thus higher acceptability with physicians.
- *Communication and education critical.* Whichever guidelines the managed care organization employs, they should be understood by the providers. High denial rates and excessive phone calls do not serve either the health plan's or the provider's purpose. Yet we see relatively little activity in this regard.
- *Community standard.* Finally, providers and provider-sponsored organizations have a tendency to select different guidelines for use in utilization committees and their own utilization review activities. Typically these guidelines are less aggressive than those employed by the health plan. We recommend that the provider organization survey the major payers in its market and then adopt the most stringent set of standards. Any other approach results in an unwarranted—and actually increasing— number of denials.

Disease Management Components

Disease management embodies a systematic approach to healthcare by rationally organizing clinical and administrative resources to support the comprehensive management of patients with specific diseases across providers and various sites of services. Moreover, while it does so under virtually any payment mechanism, it particularly makes sense under at-risk financial arrangements in which a financial incentive to optimize all services, not maximize any particular service, exists.

Disease management is particularly appropriate in cases in which the targeted disease state:

- occurs with high frequency;
- is clinically complex to manage; or
- requires intense utilization of resources.

Minimally, key components of disease management include:

- evidence- or outcomes-based guidelines;
- information technology support for warehousing and analyzing outcomes and cost by disease entity;
- provider network management, including the means to achieve physician buy-in (possibly a local medical advisory board), communicate the knowledge base, and identify potential instances of nonadherence;
- a care coordinator or disease manager to coordinate services across the network; and
- systems, including financial incentives, for influencing patient behavior and optimizing compliance.

Given the central role that pharmacotherapeutics has assumed in disease management, we further believe that a pharmacy benefit management capability has become a core component.

Disease Management Challenges

In light of our earlier comments on physician relations the most significant pitfall in implementing a comprehensive disease management approach is a lack of physician buy-in. A recent report by the Boston Consulting Group (Robinson and Matheson 2000) stated succinctly that it is:

virtually impossible to impose disease management on physicians. *They must discover its benefits for themselves or work closely with colleagues that have. In fact, developing insights into how a disease should be managed is usually less difficult than changing behavior to reflect the insights.* [italics added]

Although a great many things in medicine and healthcare delivery have changed in the intervening years, the challenge referenced by this quote has not, nor is it likely to in the foreseeable future. Moreover, this challenge is double bladed. Not only must the payer or health plan be willing to engage the physician provider, but the physicians with whom the health plan would contract must have created a culture of and context for quality. For precisely this reason, for instance, BlueCross BlueShield of Illinois will only contract with reasonably well-integrated, multispecialty organizations. Form is secondary to function (the organizations might be a PC, IPA, or PHO); that is, HMO Illinois anticipates that only in some type of multispecialty form can physicians work closely enough together to understand how they need to cooperatively manage disease in a risk-bearing arrangement.

If the first significant challenge of disease management is qualitative, the second is clearly quantitative: disease management requires significant investment. Unless such investment is part of the long-term strategy of the managed care organization it will not likely be warranted. Two strategic conditions warrant such investment:

1. financial risk—the organization not only holds risk but also endorses risk management rather than risk avoidance as its key strategy; and
2. value added—the organization perceives that it must make this investment to differentiate itself in the market.

Thus, provider organizations that either accept risk or mature direct contracting strategies, as in sponsorship of a network PPO, will likely find such an investment worthwhile. Others may find it more difficult to justify.

Physician Profiling

Increasingly, not only will the essence of medical management center on physician relations, but the essence of physician relations will focus on physician profiling. Thus, it is worthwhile to describe specific various aspects of this topic. While specific content and reporting elements of physician profiles will be discussed later, the profiling function itself is the embodiment of medical management and rightly belongs under this heading.

The Challenges

That physician practice patterns vary widely, even adjusted for mortality and morbidity, should not surprise us. The notions of best clinical practice and evidence-based medicine are still in their infancy. Even on relatively straightforward matters best practices are difficult to define and may depend on the point of view. Thus, physician profiling is fraught with practical challenges. Consider, for instance, the following points.

- *The ambiguity of medical necessity.* Vast gray areas exist, within which the comorbid condition of one patient, or even a set of patients within a practice (such as diabetics), may make a visit or procedure medically desirable if not outright necessary where it otherwise may not be.
- *The challenge of statistical significance.* By the time we peel away the layers to examine like utilization of services under like circumstances, the numbers are so small as to be no longer reliable.
- *The effect of seasonality.* Conclusions rendered over periods of less than one year are subject to variability because of factors well outside the physician's control.

Finally, we should not be surprised to find wide variation in physician practice patterns simply because physicians have generally not been provided with legitimate, valid data—or even any data at all—about how their surgical and office visit rates, outcomes, and use of specific medications compare with other physicians, even where such comparisons have been reasonably made.

So Why Profile?

As patients, purchasers, and policymakers seek ways to make certain that they obtain the best value for the money spent on healthcare—value that relies upon ongoing efforts to improve the care provided by individual physicians—it is critical that we understand the "underpinnings of physician practice patterns" (Eisenberg 1986).

With recent and projected trends in the growth of office-based procedures, and particularly of prescriptions,[3] the need to understand and address physician practice patterns in order to meaningfully manage care is greater than ever. And the lessons of the literature of the past two to three decades are just as clear. As James (1993) put it, "The core problem is variation in clinical practice." Citing the work of Dr. John Wennberg, the RAND Corporation, and his own quality, utilization, and efficiency studies that demonstrated unexplainable 60 percent to 460 percent variations in "specific care factors" among surgeons in various procedures, James (1993) noted the following problems that continue to present barriers to increasing the value, and even the quality, of healthcare.

- Eighty to ninety percent of common medical practices have no basis in published scientific research.
- Much of the scientific research that does exist is not available to medical practitioners.
- Even the limited scientific information available may overwhelm the capacity of the unaided human mind.
- Humans are inherently fallible information processors.

In summarizing some of the conclusions of the literature of the 1990s (see Figure 6.4), we not only note remarkable parallels to and consistencies with conclusions of the work done in the 1980s, but we further note that we seem to be making less than optimal use of these lessons today. First, the dominance of PPOs, with their significantly

Figure 6.4 Lessons of the Literature on Heath Care Quality and the Use of Guidelines

1. The fundamental issue is variations in clinical practice patterns.
2. Real benefits accrue to patients, payers, and providers when inappropriate practice variations decline.
3. For most physicians, financial rewards are secondary to good care.
4. "Guidelines" are nothing new in American Medicine.
5. The central issue is "control."
6. Implementing process management requires a partnership.
7. Local consensus is necessary for implementing guidelines.
8. The effective use of guidelines requires feedback—using credible data.
9. Physicians will lead—if the subject is approached through existing professional values, structures, and realities.

Source: James, B. C. 1993. "Implementing Practice Guidelines Through Clinical Quality Improvement," *Frontiers of Health Services Management* 10 (1): 18.

limited ability to capture and report the data required for profiling, suggests that much of the infrastructure is not in place. Second, while consolidation of health plans has continued, some of the largest plans now prefer national over local contracting and medical management models, ignoring both the local nature of all healthcare and the need to carefully consider existing professional values, structures, and realities. Third, some plans are abandoning, at least temporarily, the idea of physician profiling altogether, apparently not understanding that the flaw lies in their means, not the end itself. Fourth, the insurer-provider partnerships of the mid-1990s seem to have been largely abandoned without alternatives to take their place.

The nine lessons of the literature highlighted in Figure 6.4 nevertheless seem to provide valid direction and guidance for proceeding, and health plans' difficulties in implementing meaningful physician profiling strategies may simply provide a window of opportunity for providers, including hospitals and health systems, to partner to do so, thus increasing the value they bring to patients and payers alike.

Two Approaches

While we will provide concrete examples later in this chapter, we will note here that two alternatives for profiling physician practice patterns exist.

Profiles based on normative data will compare a physician with his or her peers. Such comparisons may either rank physicians (by specialty or procedure as appropriate), cluster physicians in tiers, or some combination thereof. However formatted, performance is presented relative to a peer group.

Profiles based on standards will compare a physician with a clinical outcome or measure adopted as the standard for that particular procedure or protocol. Reports may or may not show results for an entire peer group. Often they will not. However formatted, performance is presented relative to an absolute standard or benchmark.

While standards-based reporting naturally lends itself to profiling performance where absolute measures exist, particularly when those measures will be used by some third party, the managed care organization will want to use some combination of the above. What makes such reports successful, however, is not the format itself, but rather whether the physicians (or their representatives) who will be profiled had input into the reports and their content.

In other words, the best report is one that is accepted as containing data that are valid, timely, and relevant. It is on these three criteria that physicians will accept or reject any profiling of their performance.

A Final Caution

The challenges of physician profiling—and the potential legal liability if done incorrectly—are so significant that some national health plans have suspended their relatively sophisticated profiling activities while they further consider the implications for their organization. And if profiling is to be used to sanction and recredential, to admonish and isolate physician behavior, such a conservative approach seems patently reasonable. If, however, profiling is undertaken with rather than against physicians as a means of managing clinical processes, outcomes, and resources rather than physicians themselves, a progressive approach is not only warranted but will evidence the mature managed care organization.

FINANCIAL MANAGEMENT

The above discussion of guidelines for sharing financial risk might serve as a preface to a consideration of financial management of the managed care organization. After considering another strategic matter—objectives of a reimbursement mechanism, which may differ from that of other healthcare organizations—this section will address the following aspects of financial management of managed care organizations:

- pricing managed care contracts;
- the role of the actuary;
- the significance of incurred-but-not-reported (IBNR) expenses; and
- sources and uses of data, including reporting and analysis, which will logically lead to a consideration of operations.

Objectives of a Reimbursement Mechanism

Precisely because no method of compensation or reimbursement can be free of financial incentives, the managed care organization must articulate the objectives of its reimbursement mechanism. Whether it communicates or otherwise makes known these objectives, the starting point for a solid financial management strategy is to honestly articulate the objectives for a payment plan so that the organization can further anticipate the implications of those objectives financially, operationally, and politically. These objectives of course will vary widely with the ownership and overall structure of the managed care organization. Usually the first, and perhaps only, objective will be expressed in terms of the medical expense ratio even though the implications go well beyond finance. Additionally, the managed care organization may have different objectives for, say, hospitals and other facilities than it does for physicians.

Following are some recommended objectives for a reimbursement mechanism.

- Effective control of overall utilization/costs
- Adequate provision of nonnetwork care
- Capacity for adverse risk absorption
- Acceptability, understandability, manageability
- Equitable distribution of dollars

We would point out that while these objectives of necessity start with a consideration of the medical expense ratio, payment mechanisms should address the larger, more encompassing issue of providing for the effective and sustainable control of overall costs and utilization.

Pricing and the Role of the Actuary

As in any industry, pricing may be the most challenging of the financial functions. It embodies the managed care organization's entire marketing as well as financial strategy. While it ultimately will rely on judgment and intuition combined with the articulation of specific marketing and financial goals, it must begin with as objective and quantifiable a process as possible.

Pricing begins with a consideration of current use and cost levels for a specific community. (Hidden under this effort are underlying objectives, whether expressed or not, about marketing strategies and objectives for that community.) If the managed care organization has no experience base, the assistance of an actuary will be a necessity. The second question then becomes "What would be the effect of both competitive pricing and the implementation of best practices on these utilization levels and costs?" In other words, what could, though not necessarily will, be achieved in a so-called perfect world? Then comes the question of what will be achieved—the answer to which will be driven by an estimate of the potential effectiveness of the proposed delivery system, an answer that relies upon the active involvement and engagement of the physician community, which in turn is a function of both the physician community's experience with managed care in general and the physician relations program of the managed care organization in question. Once these estimates are in place refinements based on specific benefit designs can be incorporated and cost models projected.

Note that this process implies a multiyear strategy for moving from where the community is to where it can be in the future. As such, we recommend a rolling three-year pro forma.

The Effect of Incurred-But-Not-Reported Expenses

As discussed in chapter 5, because of the lag in billing, at-risk managed care organizations will have incurred medical expenses at any given time that have not yet been reported (i.e., IBNR). The size of the risk pool and experience base of the managed care organization will determine the effect that IBNR will have on reporting. In short, the practical implication, particularly for most provider-sponsored organizations, is that IBNR will require a 60- to 90-day lag in reporting, a lag that most provider organizations will find themselves unaccustomed to.

Sources and Uses of Data

In the end, the true value that the managed care organization brings to the market derives neither from its role as a care deliverer nor as a financing organization. It is not as either provider or insurer, but only as a knowledge-based organization that the value of its output can exceed the sum of its input. But in order to operate in this way, the managed care organization must aggregate data so that it transforms delivery and financing insights into knowledge and then acts on that knowledge. Thus, in a managed care organization sources and uses of data become as important as sources and uses of dollars.

Managed care organizations historically have relied on four key sources of data (see Figure 6.5), each of which has corresponding

Figure 6.5: A Consideration of Alternative Data Sources

Source	Advantages	Disadvantages

CLAIMS and ENCOUNTER FORMS	– Availability/Access
	– Cost Effectiveness
	– Volume
	– Statistical Significance
	– Historic (Longitudinal)
		– Population Instability
		– Lack of Completeness
		  Population not captive
		  Claims submission/lag
		  Non-covered services
		– Accuracy
		  Upcoding/miscoding
		  Unbundling
		– Submission Lag
		– Depth (What, not why)

MEDICAL RECORDS	– Completeness – Depth	– Cost of Accessing – Site Fragmentation
SURVEYS	– Consumer Oriented – Increasingly validated and standardized	– Hawthorne Effect – Cost of Conducting – Sample Sizes – Relevance to Physician
OUTCOMES STUDIES	– Depth – Specificity	– Cost – Difficulty Isolating Variables

advantages and disadvantages. Principally because of the overwhelming applicability and availability of claims data, claims have provided the preponderant share of such data. Increasingly, however, we expect this to change somewhat for two reasons.

First, information technology seems to be on the verge of enabling the electronic medical record technically, financially, and organizationally. As this format becomes more widely adopted over the next several years, cost-effective access to the more clinically vibrant and descriptive data it contains will enhance its usefulness for disease management and physician profiling activities.

Second, some managed care organizations have found that self-reported health status is the best predictor of cost and utilization as well as the most useful source of information for proactive case management programs. Thus, next-generation managed care organizations enabled by interactive hardware, such as the Internet, and software technologies, such as application service providers, will increase the use of health risk appraisals both prospectively (for forecasting) and retrospectively (for outcomes management).

Finally, managed care organizations have made selective use of various types of surveys targeted at both customers and providers. Again, technology will likely increase the utilization of such surveys as it makes them more cost effective and allows targeting to specific populations.

Although we could probably identify or create several strata of detail in reporting structures for managed care organizations, three will do. Each indicates the organization's performance at a specific level.

Macro-Level Reporting

We begin with the traditional financial reporting forms—the balance sheet, statement of expenses and revenues, sources and uses of funds, etc., which apply to managed care organizations as to any others (except for the additional presence of an IBNR calculation or estimation as earlier noted). These are the summaries that a board of trustees or managers will ordinarily review every month. Overall they reflect how the plan is performing quantitatively. To oversimplify somewhat, these reports will typically organize: (1) revenues by product and nonproducts; and (2) expenses by administrative and medical, each of which will have specific categories, although these are generally somewhat unique to the organization. (The so-called medical expense:cost ratio derives from dividing medical expenses by total expenses.)

To such reports, however, we suggest adding qualitative reports that a board traditionally may not review but that may actually be more predictive of future performance and more in keeping with a board's true role. Particularly in risk-based managed care organizations, for instance, member retention, or conversely turnover rates, will forecast future performance. Plans with high membership turnover are unlikely to be able to control their medical expense ratio. Additional measures are indicators of medical outcomes, patient satisfaction, or plan management measures.

In addition to their predictive value, however, and particularly for nonprofit organizations, the inclusion of qualitative measures will reflect the organization's progress on its true mission and serve as a means for measuring and communicating such progress.

Mid-Level Reporting

Analysis of the managed care organization's performance needs to simultaneously take place along three dimensions or from three perspectives. Properly constructed, this analysis will allow us to answer three critical and interrelated questions, each beginning with "How are we performing . . ."

- *By category of care or service.* These will include inpatient, outpatient, physician, pharmacy, and other provider classes. Each class must of course be further subdivided so that we can look, for instance, at inpatient medical or surgical versus icu or primary care versus specialist, followed by a further division by subspecialty.
- *By disease entity.* A minority of diseases will likely account for the majority of costs. The managed care organization will want to identify those that are relatively discretely discernible such as otitis media, diabetes, and asthma.
- *By contract (for at-risk provider organizations) or product (for health plans).* While provider organizations may have as many as 25, 50, or even 75 managed care contracts, the Pareto principle will hold here as elsewhere. A very small minority of contracts will account for the large majority of revenues. A comparison across risk-based contracts allows the provider organization to understand

whether a variance from expected performance derives from its own behavior or if the majority of variance derives from a single payer from a specific health plan.

Analogously, payer organizations will want to evaluate performance by provider, even where it shifts risk to the provider. Though not easily done, those provider organizations that demonstrate the most performance stability obtain financial performance feedback from the provider organizations with which they contract; and the best actually consult with the providers, dealing with them perhaps as an automotive manufacturer might look out for the best interests of a dealership out of enlightened self-interest.

Only by so delineating costs can we gain the insights required for a meaningful action plan. To be finally realized, however, such insight must derive from further bifurcating the costs in these categories. Just as we constructed a budget by first estimating a unit use rate and then applying a unit cost, so we must now deconstruct the actual financial performance into unit use and unit cost. Thus, these "unit use-cost" reports by category and subcategory provide detailed documentation about exactly what is happening and allow us to begin to frame an action plan to address variances and targeted areas of improvement.

Micro-Level Reporting

Because individual physician practice patterns represent the cellular level of performance for the managed care organization provider performance reporting represents the third tier. Rather than the starting place for evaluating performance, as some organizations seem to see it, it represents the core of where we need to be. Having established context through our mid-tier evaluation, it allows us to finally focus on the nitty gritty.

Physician profiling can be achieved in any number of ways. As previously discussed, what is important is that physicians have input into both report design and use, are comfortable with the relevancy and accuracy of the data presented (the first of which is virtually unachievable without their input), and see performance information at the individual physician level. By developing a physician profile that provides both quantitative and qualitative performance information the managed care organization reflects its interests in quality as well as cost concerns.

What kind of qualitative performance data should be provided? The answer depends on the issues that concern the individual organization and the physicians themselves. Usually the inclusion of only two to four measures is appropriate to avoid either overwhelming or diluting the importance of what is being measured.

OPERATIONS MANAGEMENT

Contract management in the provider organization that accepts no risk and sponsors no direct contracting strategies might logically involve only a means of tracking actual payments and comparing them with what was expected. Thus, managed care management may be reasonably considered strictly a financial function. Analogously, for the network PPO responsible for only provider contracting and sales managed care management may be reasonably considered strictly a marketing function. For the at-risk managed care organization, however, the range of functional responsibilities—from enrolling members and tracking benefits to providing the type of hierarchy of reporting and analysis described above—will cause operations to be seen as a function in its own right.

Key Functions and Their Coordination

Of the potential several dozens of interrelated tasks and subfunctions there are six (or seven if information systems is included in operations) key areas:

1. Eligibility processing
2. Benefits management
3. Payment processing
4. COB processing

5. Reinsurance processing
6. Customer services
7. MIS services/reporting

While at first appearance many of these activities are reasonably straightforward and consistent with those of traditional indemnity-based insurers, in fact the managed care environment adds significant complexity to them. From managing multiple payment mechanisms to supporting provider networks, operations in the managed care environment require a systems-oriented approach and recognition that in many ways administrative or operational functions are not wholly distinct from—and are actually intertwined with—the delivery of clinical care and services.

For provider-sponsored organizations that accept risk, the significance of the key areas is that all of these functions need to be put into place. Additionally, for both provider- and payer-sponsored organizations that share or shift risk a means must be created and maintained for coordination of these activities. For instance, the provider organization that obtains enrollment data from a payer some 60 or 90 days late will not be able to properly cut capitation checks, manage benefits, or adjudicate fee-for-service claims. Member and employer satisfaction will rely on the close coordination of activity between payer and provider.

Managing Operational Quality

The interdependent complexity of the functions considered above requires a strong, systematic approach to quality in support of the members, physicians, and contracted partners in the managed care organization. In addition to beginning with a commitment to the highest possible administrative standards augmented by an ongoing process of quality improvement, day-to-day operational quality will require matrices that specify contractual obligations to various partners as well as regular and ongoing audits to ensure that those obligations are being met.

Organizational Structure and Management

The various functions and subfunctions of the managed care organization can be combined in any number of logical ways. No two organizations will or necessarily should be organized alike. The functions above might be clustered together under one senior operations executive, or various components might very well be the responsibility of either the chief financial officer (e.g., claims payment) or marketing officer (e.g., client support). Our overall preference, whatever structure is employed, is to use an executive with a strong clinical background. The reason is that such a background facilitates a perspective that operations should support the clinical and medical management functions.

MANAGED MEDICAID

Our intent in contemplating managed Medicaid is not to present a detailed synopsis of requirements and case studies, but simply to consider the question of whether the same principles that we employ to create a well-managed commercial managed care organization can work within the context of Medicaid funding. Although we know of only a limited number of successful managed Medicaid programs, the same principles can clearly work if given an adequate premium structure. In some regards Medicaid (and Medicare) populations represent the ideal setting in which to apply managed care provided that there is an adequate revenue stream and an understanding that these principles must be applied in a manner specific to the consumer population to be served.

Income and Other Prerequisites

As we noted earlier, the question of adequate premium payment is a prerequisite for success. If the dollars flowing into the system are inadequate, no delivery system efficiencies or administrative techniques can make up for the inadequacy. Thus, in further considering issues and challenges with serving a Medicaid population through a managed care organization we assume that the dollars available will be more than simply a small fraction of billed charges, as is the case in many states. Moreover, other principles discussed in chapter 5 with regard to risk must be considered. The enrolled population must be of a statistically significant size, and risk must flow through the system in a fair manner to the extent that it is passed onto providers.

Delivery System

If we presume that commercially targeted health plans must exhibit a strong consumer-specific understanding and response, we should apply the same presumption to the Medicaid population. The plan must be administratively, operationally, and medically oriented to understanding and meeting the needs of the Medicaid eligible. Providers must be keenly aware of the unique social, cultural, financial, and other characteristics and needs of its population and be prepared to meet those needs in the appropriate geographic locations.

Dedicated, Proactive Providers

The managed Medicaid program with the greatest chance of success will be that with a panel of providers—physicians, physician extenders, nurse practitioners, social workers, and other providers—most dedicated to the mission and purpose at hand. If network and IPA-based HMOs have an inherent flaw or challenge, it is that providers in the panel in too many cases participate not out of a sense of dedication or commitment to the purpose of the organization but out of a sense that they must. They thus constitute an inherently compromised delivery panel that is far from likely to put forth the kind of collaborative efforts required of a managed care organization. When matters are worsened by provider relations and communications that antagonize or alienate providers, whomever is at fault, the outcome is what we see in many communities today.

Medicaid and other special-population managed care organizations may actually have an advantage in avoiding this potentially tragic flaw. They may tend to attract providers who participate because they want to rather than because they have to and whose commitment to the plan is more than financial. Such providers are more likely to be the ambassadors for the patient with the plan and vice versa. *If we could focus on but one critical success variable, this would be the one.*

Preventive Care

By enrolling the kind of providers who practice in the Medicaid community the managed care organization will have a head start in establishing a panel that provides preventive care—the kind of service that must be brought to the customer, who is unlikely to seek it in many cases.

Access and Outreach

Access, particularly in terms of providing preventive and early interventional care, will begin with a strong and viable outreach program. Services will be as decentralized and neighborhood based as possible. When necessary transportation will be provided to facilitate access and reduce barriers to care.

Integration

Key to the success of managed Medicaid organizations will be links to community-based social service and religious organizations. Such links represent the kind of systems approach discussed earlier and can provide for a more holistic continuum of care than most commercially based organizations.

Education

The managed care organization serving the Medicaid population faces unique challenges for educating its members with regard to seeking and following up on care. By itself it is less likely to meet these challenges than if it integrates with locally based services or religious organizations that are well-established and trusted.

INFORMATION SYSTEMS

We identified information systems in addressing the attributes of successful managed care organizations near the beginning of this chapter, perhaps too obviously. Yet perhaps not. Major health plans across the country have, in recent years and even today, either been brought to their knees or continued to frustrate their customers because of information systems issues. Similarly hospitals and provider organizations continue to view information systems problems outside the paradigm of change, attempting to make their inpatient-oriented systems function in the world of managed care.

The Essence of Form Following Function

More than a function of finance or a tool of operations, we must view information systems in the context of the concepts that underlie them. As Peter Drucker (1995) wrote in a timeless article on the information executives need to do their jobs and lead their organizations, information systems should:

> convert what were always seen as discrete techniques to be used in isolation and for separate purposes into one integrated information system. That system then makes possible business diagnosis, business strategy, and business decisions. That is a new and radically different view of the meaning and purpose of information: as a measurement on which to base future action rather than as a postmortem and a record of what has already happened.

If, as we have argued, managed care organizations compete as knowledge-based organizations, information systems represent the essence of the systematic approach to healthcare financing and delivery. The are used to empower provider and executive alike by providing insights on which to base future actions. They become the key to creating what Senge (1990) wrote so intelligently about, "learning organizations"—organizations that "tap into people's commitment and capacity to learn at *all* levels of the organization." Learning organizations gradually peel away at root causes rather than responding to monthly or even daily crises with knee-jerk reactions. They take the time to develop the required reporting hierarchy discussed earlier and then have the confidence in their own mission and values and the vision to trust the people who actually do the work, whether that is the claims processor or the physician, the case manager or the member services associate. They distribute information widely along the lines of the hierarchy presented above and reward the people who use it with pay for performance. In other words, the true value of information systems cannot be realized under the traditional command-and-control style that emerged from our military models and continues to live on in most organizations, particularly healthcare with its strict hierarchies and class structures. As Drucker (1995) put it:

> *The command-and-control organization that first emerged in the 1870s might be compared to an organism held together by its shell. The corporation that is now emerging is being designed around a skeleton: information, both the corporation's new integrating system and its articulation.*

The Evolution of Solutions and Problems

The challenges of finding ways to communicate in business simply reflect that larger, more ubiquitous challenge of human communications. T. S. Eliot addressed this challenge in *Four Quartets* (1950):

> *So here I am, in the middle way, having had twenty years . . .*
> *Trying to use words, and every attempt*
> *Is a wholly new start, and a different kind of failure*
> *Because one has only learnt to get the better of words*
> *For the thing one no longer has to say, or the way in which*
> *One is no longer disposed to say it.*

Perhaps nowhere in human society today is this same dilemma more evident and constant than in information systems. It seems that the very moment that newly developed information systems or productions offer a solution to the problems that plague us the problem has changed and the systems are rendered once again inadequate to the task. At a time of rapidly changing technology combined with shifting competitive circumstances and ongoing consolidation—presenting two of the most perplexing possible integration challenges, merging cultures and applications—we probably live in a time of technologic dilemma. While we have never had the current availability of systems solutions, devising a plan with which to choose among and configure those options into a practical approach may never have been more daunting.

Some organizations will choose among options based on a best-of-breed philosophy. Others will patently reject that approach in favor of a more common platform. In our view either approach will only be correct insofar as it fits with the overall corporate strategy, philosophy, and culture. Either approach may work or fail in the broader context of corporate consistency, and both will certainly fail without it. The correctness is not inherent in the approach itself, but in its context. That said, however, we will recommend several guidelines for addressing information systems challenges.

Respect the Nature of the Business

In earlier chapters we attempted to establish that while the managed care business has roots in both healthcare delivery and financing, it represents a third, distinctly different business. This discrete nature is evidenced most vividly in information systems. The provider organization, or for that matter the insurer, that would succeed in managed care (particularly on a risk-contract basis) must first and foremost respect the business purpose of the managed care organization. Neither hospital-based charge-capture systems or "punch-and-pay" indemnity claims systems will prove adequate to the complex, interdependent functions of the managed care organization.

All job functions derive from the hybrid challenges of arranging and managing the financing, delivery, and management of care and require uniquely and purposefully derived solutions. Retrofitting information systems that evolved to meet the specialized needs of either the hospital or indemnity insurer will surely fall short of meeting the needs of the managed care organization.

Do Not Make It

Underlying philosophy aside, unless your organization has a core competency and history of success in creating information systems, the most obvious advice with regard to the configuration is to not even think about creating the required solutions yourself. A merely adequate system available in the market now will serve incomparably better than the perfect system that still exists as a concept.

No Single Vendor

The complexity of the managed care organization's internal and external environments—integrating as they must clinical, financial, operational, and marketing functions—extends well beyond any current vendor's capabilities. Particularly for the provider organization seeking to create the integrated delivery system, this reality will argue for an overall architecture of system design. Even when, as seems reasonable, the managed care organization builds around a central or primary vendor for the major functions—those associated with hospital, physician practices, and managed care—multiple adjunctive systems will be required for special needs and functions.

Purchase on Three Criteria

A relatively straightforward triad of questions serves well in systems selection.

First, how well does the information system under consideration fit functionally with the identified needs of both today and tomorrow?

What kind of flexibility do we or may we need to support multiple payment mechanisms and contractual terms? Does it support major activities such as credentialing and recredentialing? Because it is unlikely that it will equally meet all of our functional needs, how do it strengths align with our priorities?

Second, what risks do we run with this particular vendor and system? Profile both the organization for financial and staffing stability as well as its ability to implement on time and enhance its products. Profile the system for leading-edge, though perhaps not cutting-edge, technology as well as experience in interfaces with other systems and organizations. Because no single vendor will likely be able to meet the myriad needs, how has the vendor in the past plugged the holes most important to your managed care organization, and how will you want them solved for yourself? Can the vendor pull it off?

Third, aside from the traditional ongoing versus one-time cost analysis, what internal costs will be generated for education, implementation, and ongoing support?

Respect the Local Nature of Healthcare

A senior vice president of one of the larger national payers who has responsibilities for provider contracting recently told us that his managed care organization's approach is to "go to where the physician is." If the physicians are well-organized and multidisciplinary such that they can manage risk, the managed care organization executes a partial (physician services) capitation contract. If they have a contract or partnership with a hospital or health system as well as other delivery and management infrastructure, they will execute a global cap contract. If the physician community is fragmented, they contract on a fee-for-service basis, delegating none of the functions they otherwise would under the first scenarios. Other national plans take a one-size-fits-all approach based on the philosophy that their particular approaches—both clinical and administrative—represent the best possible practices and should therefore be universally applied.

Obviously the resolution of a centralized versus decentralized protocol is fundamental to the question of information systems.

Interestingly, at least one nationally known health plan that attempts to impose a one-size-fits-all approach does so for no other, and no better, reason than that of information systems constraints. Although not typically understood—and certainly not represented by the regional contracting staff in negotiations when they present a take-it-or-leave-it persona to providers—this plan's entire business strategy, including physician relations, is essentially established by the information systems department. While our first inclination might be to say that this is the worst possible reason to require uniformity, it may actually be the one valid reason, though not necessarily the most market driven or therefore successful. At least the plan does not overextend itself operationally and for the most part delivers on what it promises.

CONCLUSION

Healthcare's purchasers are for the first time beginning to acquire and compensate for provider services based on specific standards of performance. Even when those performance standards are limited to price, the same principles transforming other industries—a systems approach, total quality management and continuous improvement, and empowerment of the knowledge worker—offer the only sustainable strategy for competing on that basis. These principles will be tangibly evidenced in the operations of the successful managed care organization.

As such, the organization's functions must be viewed as interdependent in order to employ these principles. The fact that these functions are achieved through a provider-payer contract in no way diminishes that interdependence. Rather it accentuates it, demanding the highest possible level of collaboration between both parties for either to be fully effective. At the very center of this collaboration must be a sophisticated and realistic approach to provider relations, particularly with physicians. These relations, always personal above all else, must be supported by information systems and reporting that both represent and realize the overall functional integration.

Through thorough, legitimate, and resource-intensive research and development programs a few of the national health plans have developed medical management guidelines, algorithms, and models that can quite reasonably be presented as benchmark, and even universally applicable, approaches. These models employ the best of evidence-based outcomes and disease management protocol. They benefit from objective, nationally based studies and are simultaneously exempt from the local politics and clinical biases of any given medical community. They completely deserve to be reflected in the various terms of managed care contracts that articulate provider responsibilities and payer rights. Properly implemented, they would likely result in benefit to provider, payer, purchaser, and member alike. And yet to attempt to do so unilaterally—without negotiation or consideration of local needs, values, and perspectives—is exactly the wrong thing to do.

NOTES

1. As a response to the often-heard objection that health plans and purchasers do not care about and do not, despite occasional lip service, purchase based on quality but only on cost, we offer three observations. First, providers have obfuscated the question of quality for so long that we will have to demonstrate that it exists as an issue in the market before a skeptical buyer responds. In order to do so we will have to convince them of our standards, use theirs, or use a combination of both. Second, various organizations going back almost a decade to the National Demonstration Project on Quality in Healthcare have clearly demonstrated that an emphasis on quality and quality improvement provides the only sustainable cost-control strategy. Even if it is true that payers buy only on cost, quality improvement becomes even more critical. Third, and perhaps most importantly, we believe that a mission statement should represent the organization's most profound beliefs and intents, even if those beliefs are not necessarily rewarded in the market. To spend time elaborating on how payers only care about cost is to waste time.

2. We prefer to define PCPs by function rather than specialty. However, in general primary care will include family practice, general internal medicine, and pediatric physicians. Like Kongstvedt (1989) and others, we

recommend treating obstetricians/gynecologists as specialists, although in a gated system the managed care organization will want to allow more open access to these particular specialists for women. For a discussion of PCP staffing ratios see "Primary Care in Closed Panels" in *The Managed Care Handbook* (Kongstvedt 1989).

3. From 1988 to 1998 not only did the ingredient cost per prescription more than double for commercial HMOs, but, as significantly, the number of prescriptions per member per year in commercial HMOs increased by more than 40 percent. In comparison, Medicare HMO scripts per member per year increased by 8 percent from 1994 to 1998 (Aventis Pharmaceuticals 2000).

REFERENCES

Aventis Pharmaceuticals. 2000. *Managed Care Digest Series 2000/Managed Care Trends Digest*. Parsippany, NJ: Aventis Pharmaceuticals.

Block, P. 1993. *Stewardship: Choosing Service over Self Interest*. San Franciso: Berrett-Koehler.

Dartmouth Medical School. 2000. *Dartmouth Atlas of Health Care 2000*. Chicago: American Hospital Association.

Drucker, P. F. 1966. *The Effective Executive*. New York: Harper & Row.

Drucker, P. F. 1995. "The Information Executives Truly Need." *Harvard Business Review* 73 (January-February): 54–62.

Eisenberg, J. M. 1986. *Doctor's Decisions and the Cost of Medical Care*. Chicago: Health Administration Press.

Eliot, T. S. 1950. "East Coker." In "Four Quartets." *T. S. Eliot: the Complete Poems and Plays*. New York: Harcourt Brace and Co.

Governance Committee. 1993. "The Grand Alliance: Vertical Integration Strategies for Physicians and Health Systems." Washington, DC: Advisory Board Company.

Herzberg, F. 1966. *Work and the Nature of Man*. New York: Thomas Crowell Company.

James, B. C. 1993. "Implementing Clinical Practice Guidelines Through Clinical Quality Improvement." *Frontiers of Health Services Management* 10 (1): 3–38.

Kongstvedt, P. 1989. *The Managed Care Handbook.* Gaithersburg, MD: Aspen.

Robinson, T. and D. Matheson. 2000. "Disease Management Takes Flight." Boston Consulting Group. [On-line information; Retrieved 11/2/00]: http:// www.bcg.com/publications/ publications_splash.asp.

Senge, P. M. 1990. *The Fifth Discipline: The Art and Practice of the Learning Organization.* New York: Doubleday.

Wennberg, J., Dartmouth Medical School. 1977. Presentation at the American Hospital Association's annual meeting.

CHAPTER 7

The Future of Managed Care Contracting and Healthcare Services

"Let us not go over the old ground. Let us rather prepare for what is to come."

—*Marcus Tullius Cicero (106–43 B.C.)*

INTRODUCTION: Managed care has largely been credited with eliminating the double-digit healthcare premium increases of the 1980s and 1990s. According to the consulting firm William M. Mercer, "There can be no doubt that managed care has, at least to this point, met or exceeded employers' expectations for cost reductions. Adjusted for inflation, the average cost of insuring an employee through an employer-sponsored health plan is actually less than it was in 1993" (AFSCME 1998).

During this time health plans were using various tools to control costs, including (but not limited to):

- Developing 24-hour stay programs for maternity care. These programs usually involved discharging a mother within 24 hours of delivery for normal births or 72 hours for cesarean deliveries and providing follow-up home care by a nurse.
- Reducing unnecessary hospital stays through precertification programs. These programs resulted in eliminating many unnecessary days in the hospital (e.g., admissions immediately before surgery to do workups needing only ancillary services, admissions for surgery that could be done on an outpatient basis).
- Using the primary care physician as a "gatekeeper" and requiring

the member to get written referrals from the primary physician to see a specialist.

- Limiting use of services only to network providers and using narrow networks of providers in an effort to drive volume to those providers in return for favorable pricing.
- Using capitation payment methods to reimburse primary physicians, and later specialists, in an effort to reduce utilization.
- Paying for emergency services only when they were bona fide emergencies (as retrospectively determined by the health plan).

Many of these practices led to restricting access to care in some fashion and resulted in negative public reaction. The media seized on anecdotal reports of "horror stories," which has led to the widespread belief that there is an anti–managed care sentiment on the part of those enrolled in managed care plans. The implication is that managed care enrollees are not as happy with their plans as enrollees in traditional indemnity insurance. There is a particular opinion that those who are in poor to fair health are not satisfied with their care, whereas those in good health are satisfied. However, the facts do not seem to support this belief. Surveys conducted by the National Research Corporation in 1996 and 1997 showed comparable overall satisfaction rates for those in poor to fair health for HMOs, preferred provider organizations, and fee-for-service plans (American Association of Health Plans 1998)

The perception of considerable abuse in the managed care system has led to significant legislative intervention in the form of mandates and "patient protection" legislation. These interventions include:

- minimum lengths of stay for mothers following delivery and for women following a mastectomy;
- mandatory point-of-service (POS) product offerings;
- mental health parity (i.e., subjecting mental illness to the same benefit coverage as other illnesses);
- individual mandates such as requirements to offer men over age 40 testing for prostate cancer or to provide coverage for temporomandibular disorders, diabetes supplies, and certain drugs;

- the "reasonable person" test for use of the emergency room; and
- requirements to inform members of the payment methods being used and how the incentives might affect their care.

The good contributed to the healthcare delivery system in the United States by managed care was overshadowed by the media and legislative siege launched on the industry for its aggressive practices. During this time frame, health plans were emphasizing not only reducing costs, but also the measurement of wellness initiatives designed to prevent illness. When compared with traditional indemnity insurance, results for HMOs in this arena were significantly better. Managed care is gradually shifting the focus of the American healthcare delivery system to prevention.

CURRENT PRODUCTS

Managed care will not and cannot go away because it has changed forever how we buy and sell health. The only question is how it will evolve to measure the pulse of its customers and implement products to meet their needs. The 1990s offered a strong economy and low unemployment, affecting what customers wanted and could afford.

During that period of good economic times choice became important to the customer. New products or benefit designs offered more choice and at the same time retained the benefits of the HMO. For example, HMOs implemented POS products, which allow members to use providers who are not in the network provided they pay more when they do so. Open-access products have also made their entry into the healthcare marketplace, allowing members to go directly to specialists without first obtaining a primary care physician's referral. This eliminates the referral "hassle factor" that upsets members of traditional HMOs.

Pharmacy costs rose sharply during the 1990s. To counter this rising cost many health plans implemented formularies. These drug lists contain a sufficient mix of drugs to handle all clinical situations; however, not all drugs are a covered benefit. Patients and physicians alike reacted negatively to this restriction on choice. As a result health plans are now implementing three- or four-tiered copayment structures (see Figure 7.1). Under these systems patients can receive any drug they need or brand they want, but the cost varies depending on whether the drug is on the formulary. These types of benefit designs provide members with needed services for minimal cost but allow them the freedom to choose different providers or services for greater out-of-pocket cost.

FUTURE COMMERCIAL PRODUCTS

During difficult economic times with higher unemployment rates, inflation, and less disposable income, employers and members will opt for price; choice will become less of a consideration. Thus, in such an economy POS plans will not experience significant growth, whereas HMO plans will. There will be an ebb and flow between these types of products given the state of the economy.

The next generation of managed care products will be structured to address any economic state and put more pressure than ever on the providers of care to be high quality and low cost. Third-party payers have largely taken the members of health plans out of the decision-making process when it comes to cost and quality. The product of the future will need to re-engage the member in the process by forcing them to make cost/quality decisions.

One way of doing this is to design either the premium structure or benefit structure in a way that gives the member incentive to select lower-cost, higher-quality providers. Under the present systems, premiums or copayments are the same regardless of the network providers selected by the member. However, the cost to the plan varies greatly based on provider practice patterns, which involve not only utilization rates of services but also the cost of specialists and the hospitals or outpatient facilities to which providers refer members. The third-party payment system has insulated the member from the practice pattern costs associated with the physician chosen to provide services.

Today's health plan members must choose their providers from a directory that gives no indication of quality. The member has to

Figure 7.1: Examples of Tiered Copayment Systems

Three-tiered Copayment System	Four-tiered Copayment System
$10 all generic drugs	$15 branded drugs on the formulary
$15 branded drugs on the formulary	$30 all other drugs other than life-enhancing drugs
$30 all other drugs	$40 life-enhancing drugs (not necessary for acute conditions, e.g., impotency, hair loss)
$10 all generic drugs	

rely on word of mouth or the scant information provided by the plan (e.g., board-certification status, whether the physician speaks a foreign language). The product of the future may take these practice variations into consideration. It will also give the member some indicators of quality to assist them in making their selection.

While the ultimate model will vary depending on the market maturity or information systems capabilities of the health plan, the following models suggest possible ways of achieving this new product design.

Differing Copayment Structures

In this model, all providers in the community will be included in the provider directory. Members will select their physicians, who will be listed with both quality and cost indicators. The quality indicators will be the result of member satisfaction surveys and clinical profiling initiatives. The cost indicators will be the result of severity-adjusted utilization patterns including hospital and specialist utilization and cost.

Similar to restaurant guides, the provider directory might place a varying number of dollar signs next to a physician's name based on how much the member would have to pay to see that physician. Members who select physicians with one dollar sign might have a

$10 copayment, while two dollar signs might mean a $20 copayment. Similar structures can be developed for hospitals and ancillary services. Members will have the freedom to select any physician they want; their payment just varies depending on the cost to the plan.

Differing Premium Levels

This model also pays providers based on a system other than global capitation, and is similar to the one discussed above, with one exception. The members will pay premium levels based on which physicians they want to use. For example, if the member wants to use only physicians with one dollar sign, their premium would be $100 per month; with one or two dollar signs the premium would be $120 per month; with one, two, or three dollar signs the premium would be $150; etc.

In another model, paying providers global capitation would allow different health systems or physician-hospital organizations (PHO) to compete using global capitation. The health system or PHO could arrange to accept global capitation and members would be required to select one health system or PHO for their care. The member's premium would be determined by the cost to the plan of the health system or PHO. This model is particularly attractive to health plans in mature markets where several competing organized health systems exist. Such a model will put significant pressure on the PHO or health system to differentiate itself, particularly if its price is higher than the competition. It might also be attractive for the PHO interested in using global capitation or percent of premium to manage the care of a defined population.

NOT "BUYER BEWARE" BUT "BEWARE THE BUYER"

These changes in products represent a shift from a wholesale marketing model to a retail marketing model for healthcare. No longer will volume rely on the execution of contracts with payers alone; it will rely on a provider organization's ability to respond to the individual consumer in a manner in which it has not previously had to do.

The retailing of healthcare—finally placing healthcare in the same marketing league as other consumer-driven industries—probably represents the third of three phases that have occurred since the advent of health insurance. The first began with the indemnification of consumers in the 1930s. This phase, particularly with the entry of the federal government as indemnity insurer under Medicare, provided the economic fuel for growing the healthcare industry we know today. It also put providers squarely in charge, allowing them to determine what services would be provided where, by whom, and at what prices. Moreover, as one colleague reflecting on the poor efficiency of the industry at the time (just prior to prospective payment) put it, "We could lose half our supplies from the loading dock to the nursing floors and still make money."

The uncontrolled success of indemnity insurance and cost-plus reimbursement, of course, resulted in the unsustainable inflation in healthcare that brought about the next phase. Wrestling control away from perturbed payers, health plans asserted their dominance. Symbolically and legislatively born with the 1973 HMO act, this second phase represented the growth of wholesale contracting and the (generally selective) shifting of risk to providers. This second phase continues today, but we can probably anticipate its transition to the third phase, the age of retail healthcare.

A generation of baby boomers is now demanding of healthcare what they have recieved from other service industries: instant service and mass customization. Aided by the technology that makes these things possible, phase three is being unveiled. Only when consumers themselves put significant dollars at stake, however, are we likely to see true consumer-driven healthcare and the transformation of a provider-driven industry. Until then, hospitals will have more incentives to serve physicians and physicians will generally be able to work the system to their own advantage rather than the consumer's.

THE FUTURE IS NOW

The following example illustrates how the industry is already moving into the third phase, the retailing of healthcare. Several large employers formed Buyer's Healthcare Action Group in the Minneapolis and St. Paul area in 1991 (*Managed Care* 1998). In 1998 they formed a self-funded product called Choice Plus. Its members can select a primary care physician from any one of 24 health systems or networks at three different prices. Controls have been put in place to adjust payment to the care systems quarterly either up or down based on changes in risk profiles. This protects the care system from adverse selection, which could occur in this model. Networks are rated with one to three stars for member satisfaction and one to three dollar signs for cost, allowing the member to see for the first time some relationship between cost and quality. The pressure is on the network to improve satisfaction levels and provide services at a reasonable cost or suffer the loss of patients. Each care system or network is given a per-member-per-month budget to deliver the services. There are no referral requirements beyond what the care system places on itself, and providers are free to take care of their patients without running the gauntlet of traditional managed care rules.

THE FUTURE OF MEDICARE CHOICE+ PRODUCTS

Of the 309 plans serving Medicare beneficiaries at the end of 1999, 99 terminated contracts or reduced the number of counties they would serve in 2000. For 2001, 118 plans will terminate contracts or reduce service areas (Levin-Epstein 2000). This exit has caused concern about the future viability of Medicare HMOs.

Member satisfaction among Medicare HMO enrollees appears to be as good as or better than that with traditional Medicare coverage. Plan benefits and costs appear to be the primary reasons for these results (*Managed Care* 1998). Most Medicare HMOs offer improved benefits at little or no additional premium to the Medicare member. Some plans offer enhanced benefits (e.g., pharmacy benefits at higher limits than those offered by their basic HMO product) for an additional premium. The future of the Medicare HMO will hinge on three factors:

1. The ability of the HMOs to control utilization and cost;
2. The increase in payment rates from the Medicare program; and

3. The plans' modification of benefits offered, increase of the premiums charged for the benefits provided, or a combination of the two.

It is unlikely that rate increases from Medicare will provide sufficient revenue increases to cover the cost of the benefits being offered. Thus, the plan's ability to control utilization and cost will be critical for Medicare HMOs to be successful in making up this shortfall. This will necessitate partnerships between health plans and providers to develop the management tools necessary to control utilization and cost.

To the extent that Medicare HMOs are unable to control utilization or cost sufficiently to overcome shortfalls in revenues from Medicare, it will be necessary to either reduce the enhanced benefits or increase premiums to pass on the cost to Medicare members; the likely scenario is a combination of the two. Congress will be reluctant to take any direct action to limit benefits or increase costs. However, Congress may be willing to let the health plans do this for them. The cost of the Medicare program can be shifted to Medicare eligibles who want the better coverage the HMOs offer over traditional Medicare, a way of moving Medicare eligibles to pay for more of their healthcare costs over a period of time. A direct tax increase to support Medicare can be avoided through the use of marketplace pricing.

CONCLUSION

As managed care moves slowly and reluctantly to its next phase, the age of the consumer, it is important that the environment that has led to innovative changes not be diminished. Legislative initiatives that take away health plans' ability to develop new innovative products or delivery models, or mandate certain types of products or delivery models will work counter to the development of a market-driven response and generally serve to increase costs.[1] Rather, the goal should be encouraging managed care organizations to continue to experiment and develop new delivery models or products that build on their strengths while protecting the customer from abuses.

NOTE

1. At the time of this writing at least one state is creating a pooled risk fund for underwriting new, inexpensive products in an effort to sponsor a new option for small groups. Without regard to the irony of the situation, in order to help keep the costs as low as possible, the state is appealing to the federal government to have the pool governed under ERISA and thereby exempted from state-mandated benefits.

REFERENCES

American Association of Health Plans. 1998. "Dispelling Managed Care Myths." Washington, DC: AAHP.

American Federation of State, County and Municipal Employees (AFSCME), AFL-CIO. 1998. "Health Benefit Costs Rise in 1997." *Collective Bargaining Reporter.* [Online article; retrieved 9/4/01]. *http://www.afscme.org/wrkplace/cbr198_3.htm*

Levin-Epstein, M. 2000. "Quick Fix May Be in Store for M+C, but Meaningful Change Likely to Wait." *Managed Care* 9 (10): 16–17.

Managed Care. 1998. "Health Plans Stream Out of Medicare While Medicare+Choice Starts Slowly." *Managed Care* 7 (11): 26–28.

Appendix:
Sample Managed Care Contract
Checklist

Agreement Section	Provider Preference	HMO/ PPO
General Provisions		
It is recommended that the main body of the contract define the general terms governing the relationship. An appendix that governs the payment relationship should be developed. This structure makes the contract easier to use, particularly where different payment arrangements exist for different managed care products (e.g., preferred provider organization [PPO], point of service, HMO, Medicare + Choice [M+C] HMO, workers' compensation, managed indemnity).		
Does contract alter physician practice method of delivery or type of care rendered?	No	
Does contract limit volume of services (e.g., geography, ancillary services)?	No	
Is PHO the primary or exclusive entity?	Yes	
Entities included: all system hospitals, home health/durable medical equipment, lab, and hospice	Yes	
Definitions		
Are key terms clearly defined and acceptable to PSO?		

Created in cooperation with MidAmerica Cardiology.

Agreement Section	Provider Preference	HMO/ PPO
"Basic health care services"	Yes	
"Covered services" "Capitation"	Yes Yes	
"Clean claim" A suggested definition of a clean claim is: "A claim is deemed to be clean if provider has not received written notice to the contrary from plan or payer within xx days of receipt of the claim." As an alternative the M+C definition should be used: "A 'clean' claim is a claim that has no defect of impropriety, including lack of required substantiating documentation for non-contracting suppliers and providers, or particular circumstances requiring special treatment that prevents timely payment from being made on the claim" (Section 1842 (c)(2)(B) of the Social Security Act). A claim is clean even though the M+C organization refers it to a medical specialist within the M+C organization for examination. If additional substantiating documentation (e.g., medical record, encounter data) involves a source outside the M+C organization, the claim is not considered "lean.	Yes	
"Member or insured"	Yes	
"Utilization review"	Yes	
"Emergency services" or "emergency"	Yes	

Agreement Section	Provider Preference	HMO/ PPO
"Medically necessary services" should be defined as healthcare services that a reasonably prudent physician would deem necessary for the diagnosis or treatment of illness or injury or to improve the functioning of a malformed body member.	Yes	
"Plan" and "payer" (if the plan has arrangements allowing other payers to access plan's network) Discount clubs are excluded	Yes	
Products covered under the agreement including network rentals	Yes	
"Network" modification of the network should permit the PSO to renegotiate the rates based on the new network and effect on the expected volume.	Yes	
Plan Obligations		
Are managed care organization (MCO) policies incorporated by reference or attached?	Attached	
If by reference, are they provided?	Yes	
Are any admission requirements clearly defined?	Yes	
Can PSO terminate agreement immediately if disagreements on policy or procedure changes cannot be resolved?	Yes	
Must the MCO notify PSO in writing of any new plans or payers joining the agreement?	Yes	

Agreement Section	Provider Preference	HMO/ PPO
The patient-channeling mechanism is clearly defined (e.g., copayment differential of at least 20%, out-of-pocket maximum only applies to in-network services, the network will be limited to the following hospitals).	Yes	
Are network provider directories provided annually?	Yes	
Are notices sent for incoming and outgoing network providers?	Yes	
Are all plan payers listed in agreement and updated as changes occur?	Yes	
Can PSO terminate a payer for cause (late payments) from the MCO agreement yet keep the agreement intact with the other payers?	Yes	
Plan agrees to give PSO at least 60 days notice before new or revised benefit plans to which this contract applies are implemented [as copayment amounts may change, thereby increasing provider liability, or other incentives redirecting patients to other providers may occur] and give PSO option to terminate or renegotiate.	Yes	
Can PSO opt out of new plans added to the MCO agreement after the agreement is first signed?	Yes	
Are all participating hospitals listed in the agreement?	Yes	

Agreement Section	Provider Preference	HMO/ PPO
Health plans should provide PSO with physician-specific customer-satisfaction and quality-information reports and data for analysis to assist with medical management. For capitation or percent-of-premium arrangements plans must electronically submit all billing and eligibility information at least on a monthly basis to the PSO. If the plan fails to submit information for more than 60 days, the contract automatically reverts to a predetermined fee-for-service arrangement.	Yes	
Does plan limit their audit capability to one year?	Yes	
Plan agrees to designate a claims contact person with authority to resolve claims issues.	Yes	
Does the plan retain the right to carve out future services and contract separately for them (e.g., metal health, vision care)?	No	
If yes, does hospital or provider retain either a right to participate in carve outs or right of first refusal to retain the business?	Yes	
PSO Hospital and Physician Obligations		
Are PSO providers limited in terms of referrals allowed to be accepted?	No	
Can enrollees refer themselves directly to PSO providers?	No	
Can PSO providers refer to other PSO providers?	Yes	

Agreement Section	Provider Preference	HMO/PPO
In other than discount-off-of charge arrangements payers should not be able to request a hospital itemized bill.		
Is it PSO's responsibility to subcontract for services not provided?	Yes	
Does PSO have to credential the subcontracting provider?	No	
Can providers transfer members at their own discretion?	No	
Do PSO physicians retain the right to run their practices in a businesslike manner, including establishing limits on certain financial classes of patients (e.g., Medicare, Medicaid)?	Yes	
PSO must notify MCO of changes in its practice within 10 days.	Yes	
Is there an antidisparagement clause?	Yes	
Is PSO termination of group not required if a PSO group member fails to meet the obligations of the agreement?	No	
Does it list all the services by CPT that physician is responsible to provide under the capitation rate?	No	
Are certain services required to be provided?	Yes	
What are PSO provider's emergency or on-call obligations?	Yes	

Agreement Section	Provider Preference	HMO/ PPO
Indemnification		
Does contract require the physician to indemnify MCO?	No	
Is it specifically stated that each party is liable for their own wrongs?	Yes	
Are PSO provider's legal and patient obligations limited to a 30-day maximum continuation of care if the plan becomes insolvent?	Yes	
Is the MCO required to post a restricted insolvency deposit in a bank?	Yes	
Does contract contain a hold-harmless clause? If included, should be reviewed by legal counsel and be mutual.	No	
Do PSO providers indemnify MCO for acts of substitute physicians?	No	
Grievance Procedures and Arbitration		
There is a clearly defined dispute-resolution procedure. Recommend the party with the concern submit it in writing to the other party. There should be a 30-day period from receipt of the issue for the steering committee or other defined group to meet and resolve the issue. If they are unable to resolve, it the CEOs of the organizations will have 30 days to resolve it. If resolution is not completed and no agreement is made to extend this 30-day period, the issue will proceed to binding arbitration.	Yes	

Agreement Section	Provider Preference	HMO/ PPO
Are there rights of appeal that involve outside agencies (e.g., utilization review)	Yes	
Are appeal rights specified in the contract?	Yes	
If the agreement is long term, is there a mechanism for handling unanticipated changes (e.g., new services added by provider, new biogenetically engineered drugs)? Suggestion: The unanticipated change is written and forwarded to the other party. The steering committee or designated group has 60 days to resolve. If unresolved, the CEOs meet and have 30 days to resolve, then binding arbitration. The agreement should contain some statement of intent regarding how these issues should be handled (e.g., for new services added the hospital agrees to charge the plan its incremental costs + 10% to implement these services as verified by the hospital's auditor)	Yes	
Continuation of Care		
Are provider's obligations limited to providing care for the remainder of the inpatient treatment or 30 days, whichever is less, if contract ends?	Yes	
Is post-contract care based on provider's usual and customary charges?	Yes	
Compensation		
It is recommended that a separate appendix be developed for each product where there are different rates involved and that these products be clearly defined. This will reduce confusion regarding payment arrangements.	Yes	

Agreement Section	Provider Preference	HMO/ PPO
If payment rates are based on diagnosis-related groups (DRG) and the contract exceeds one year in length, it should include a methodology for adjusting payment as the federal DRG grouper is changed. This will ensure that the original payment contemplated under the agreement is maintained.	Yes	
Any exclusions from the DRG or per-diem rates should be clearly delineated (e.g., t-PA [revenue code 259], implants [revenue codes 275–278], trauma]). For implants negotiate percentage off of charges rather than cost plus; this eliminates administrative hassles regarding invoices.	Yes	
Are any hospital-based physician fees within the hospital rate clearly defined (e.g., emergency room physician's charge included in the hospital emergency room bill)? General policy is not to include in hospital rates.	No	
Are there separate mother and baby case rates?	Yes	
Is there an additional nursery per diem for multiple births?	Yes	
Are observation rates defined, and when do they apply (e.g., automatically move to inpatient status after 23 hours and 59 minutes)? Clarify observation reimbursement from emergency room and outpatient surgery. Achieve reimbursement for procedures performed during observation.	Yes	

Agreement Section	Provider Preference	HMO/ PPO
Is there additional reimbursement for multiple outpatient surgeries (e.g., 100% on primary surgery, 50% on all others)?	Yes	
Is there a percentage discount on "all other inpatients and outpatients not specifically mentioned in the contract"? Is there a percentage discount on all physician fees not listed in the fee schedule?	Yes	
Is fee schedule attached?	Yes	
Are anesthesia and pain management CPT codes separate and distinct reimbursements per point rather than a % of resource-based relative value system?	Yes	
Are payment terms clearly defined? It is suggested that revenue codes be used in the contract where appropriate to clarify what is included within what rates (e.g., surgical step down [revenue code 206, 214]).	Yes	
Compensation renegotiation date specified?	Yes	
Cost of living or Consumer Price Index adjustments in contract?	Yes	
Is there a clear definition of how coordination of benefits works? It should not apply when a government contract is primary.	Yes	
Are there provisions for reimbursement to PSO-allied health professionals?	Yes	
Are reimbursement rates renegotiated yearly?	Yes	

Agreement Section	Provider Preference	HMO/PPO
Ideally changes to fee schedules should not be able to be made unilaterally. [Unlikely that most plans will agree to this as they have one fee schedule.] Where they will not agree to this, it is required that 90-day advanced notice and an opportunity to terminate the contract before the effective date of the fee change are given.	Yes	
Does contract contain a favored-nations provision? "We guarantee the physician fee schedules for calendar year X. More specifically, we will not reduce fee-for-service rates, capitation rates, or conversion factors during this time period. These rates and conversion factors are the same for all physicians of like specialties throughout the physician network in the metropolitan counties. If these rates or conversion factors are raised for any MCO physician within these counties, this increase will be extended to physicians in the like specialty."	Yes	
Is there a favored-nations provision in the agreement for hospital rates? Do other contracts exist with a favored-nations clause and is this agreement consistent with those contracts? If a favored-nations provision has been agreed to, is there a clear understanding of how this provision will be applied (e.g., if rates are per diem, this contract provision only applies to other per-diem arrangements; every year an independent auditor will verify the hospital is in compliance)?	Yes	
If sufficient evidence of coverage or referral is not presented, can practice hold member financially responsible?	Yes	

Agreement Section	Provider Preference	HMO/ PPO
Is 24–7 eligibility determination available? If not available, will plan pay when reasonable efforts are made to obtain verification (e.g., use prior list of members)?	Yes	
Are payments made within 30 calendar days of submission of claims for noncapitation contracts?	Yes	
Is MCO penalized by reverting to billed charges if late in making payments?	Yes	
Is the time limit for submission of claims at least 180 days?	Yes	
Does plan/MCO notify PSO provider within 10 days of receipt if additional claim information is needed or absent notice the claim is deemed to be clean?	Yes	
If additional information is required, does plan pay within 10 days of receipt of this information or claim reverts to billed charges?	Yes	
Capitation Issues		
Is a single rate used for all covered lives or is it adjusted?	Adjusted	
What is the type of capitation?		
Are services to be provided for the cap rate clearly defined?	Yes	

Agreement Section	Provider Preference	HMO/ PPO
Are required services to be provided within the cap payment defined? It is suggested that a matrix be developed that outlines the scope of services to be provided and which party is responsible for providing those services. It is critical that each party clearly understand exactly which services it is responsible to provide under the capitation agreement and which services are outside the agreement.	Yes	
Are any carve-out services defined?	Yes	
Can practice renegotiate cap rate at any time after 90 days?	Yes	
Is there a withhold pool?	No	
What is the amount of the withhold?		
History of distributions?	Available	
Is methodology or terms for distributions clearly defined?		
Distributions discretionary or matter of right?		
Has the distribution protocol been provided?	Yes	
Is it clearly defined how recoveries from reinsurance, coordination of benefits, and subrogation are handled?	Yes	
Are providers paid fee for service until a certain number of patients are assigned (e.g., 5,000 for specialty physicians, 350 for primary care physicians)?	Yes	

Agreement Section	Provider Preference	HMO/ PPO
Is the PSO provider credited with an enrollee for the month of entry into the plan or practice?	Yes	
Does primary care physician capitation exclude inpatient hospitalization?	Yes	
Is the capitation rate adjusted by age and sex and premium?	Yes	
Are hospitalists included in risk contracts?	Yes	
UR/QA		
Does contract provide UR/QA documentation?	Yes	
Who conducts UR?		
When will UR occur?		
What are UR criteria used?		
Is there a clause that states that all communication regarding UR/QA is deemed to be communication to a peer review committee and is therefore confidential under law?	Yes	
Is precertification required to be done only by the entity to receive payment?	Yes	
Utilization review plans essential elements: 1. All decisions to deny services shall be made by physicians. 2. Access to hospital records does not include access to UR/QA committee minutes.		

Agreement Section	Provider Preference	HMO/ PPO
3. UR program process shall be conducted in a timeframe so as not to place covered individual in a position of not electing to receive services because of one opinion.		
4. Each identification card shall clearly designate instructions and contact information pertaining to the UM agent.		
5. Plan shall respond to provider inquiries by next business day.		
6. Emergency admissions shall be authorized the next business day.		
7. Authorization of admission is the responsibility of the provider or covered individual as defined by the plan.		
8. Type of review, criteria set, and staffing plan shall be specified.		
9. Rules required of plan and provider shall be stipulated.		
10. Plan must abide by facility policies governing on-site review.		
11. Use of PSO medical director to facilitate treatment plan if dispute arises.		
12. A general outline of the following review processes shall be provided: • Preadmission review • Admission review • Continued stay review • Focused review • Quality assurance review • Discharge planning review • Ambulatory review		
13. Direct patient access should be avoided or controlled through hospital UM departments.		

Agreement Section	Provider Preference	HMO/ PPO
14. Hospitals should be able to bill patients for continued stays with written permission of patient.	Yes	
Term and Termination		
Is there an evergreen clause?	No, unless discount off of charges	
If yes, it needs to define a method for renegotiating rates and allow for renegotiation of rates during the term of the agreement. At a minimum this should occur if plan increases the number of hospitals (or providers, as defined in the agreement) in geographic area of hospital or provider of if plan carves out special services.	Yes	
Are breach-of-contract causes clearly defined (e.g., insolvency, late or improper payments)?	Yes	
Is there a cure period in event of a breach of contract?	Yes	
Is there a no-cause termination clause?	Yes	
Can the PSO terminate or not contract with selected payers?	Yes	
Any limitations on terminating contract other than time?	No	
Independent Contractors		
Does contract state that both entities are independent contractors?	Yes	

Agreement Section	Provider Preference	HMO/ PPO
Insurance		
Does contract state that both parties carry appropriate liability insurance?	Yes	
Medical Records		
Is access to administrative and accounting records restricted to members only?	Yes	
Access to information and records should include: 1. Requirement to maintain all information regarding members and providers confidential. 2. Requirement to maintain all information regarding the financial nature of the contract or business plans of either party learned as a result of the contract (e.g., at the steering committee meetings) confidential. 3. Reasonable access by plan to access records necessary to monitor the performance of provider under the contract. 4. Reasonable access by government and accrediting agencies.	Yes	
Does MCO pay for all reasonable costs of practice complying with MCO's review of medical records?	Yes	
Confidentiality		
Is there confidential information language? Proprietary information language?	Yes	

Agreement Section	Provider Preference	HMO/ PPO
Assignment of Agreement		
Can MCO assign agreement to another party? (90-day notice with the ability to cancel the contract. Mutual consent is preferred.)	Yes	
Amendments		
Can MCO amend contract or change rates or policies without physician consent (except when change is mandated by law)?	No	
If yes, can PSO terminate contract without cause prior to the effective date of the change?	Yes	
Governing Law		
Is governing law Missouri or Kansas?	Yes	
Noncompete		
Can a practice provider be employed by other healthcare firms (e.g., other healthcare agreements, consultant, paid committees, seminars)?	Yes	
Is there noncompete language relating to offering patients other plans?	No	
Stop-loss Insurance		
Does MCO pay for stop-loss insurance?	Yes	
Switch of method of payment to discounted fee for service after set loss?	Yes	
Actuarial Considerations		
Does MCO have historical actuarial data?	Yes	

Agreement Section	Provider Preference	HMO/ PPO
Has an actuarial assessment been made that demonstrates a minimum yield of the current Medicare rate if utilization assumptions are met?	Yes	
Geography distribution	Yes	
Age distribution	Yes	
Sex distribution	Yes	
Relationship Position		
Is the MCO willing to discuss the following:		
What rates do they get from employers?	Yes	
What do they take for their own profit pool?	Yes	
What amount is left over for patient care?	Yes	
How is the leftover amount split between hospitals and physicians?	Yes	
Other Items		
Is PSO delegated credentialing?	Yes	
If one of the top five or six payers, is there a steering committee from plan and PHO that meets a minimum of quarterly to address any operational issues or items requiring consensus? The committee should have the necessary authority to resolve these issues.	Yes	
What bundling software do they use? Obtain a written description of the plan's bundling practices. Require notification with option to terminate if changes are made.		

Index

mechanism, 225–26; pricing, 226–27; and macro-level reporting, 229–30; and micro-level reporting, 231–32; and mid-level reporting, 230–31
First-mover retailer, 79–80
Fixed-fee pricing, 31
Flexible budgeting, 104
Flow of funds, 126; plan retention, 127; premium payment, 127; provider payments, 127–28; reinsurance, 128

Gain sharing, 91
Gettelson, A., 146
Global risk, 13
Great Depression, 38, 43

Health Care Financing Administration, 66
Health insurance: increases in premiums, 68; indemnity, 39, 48; privatization of, 38
Health Insurance Portability and Accountability Act (HIPAA), 121
Health maintenance organizations (HMOS), 11, 16, 48, 49, 52, 58–59, 128, 132–33, 135, 140, 167, 189, 201, 249, 254–55; cost advantage, 58; enrollment in, 1–2; indemnity versus traditional, 55; and margin pricing, 23; and maturity of markets, 79–80; in the 1990s, 69–70; and open access, 69; ownership, 49; performance measures, 61; and physicians, 212

Health Plan Employer Data and Information Set (HEDIS), 68, 206, 207
Health plans: effects of copayments, 137; enrollee change ratios, 60, 62; expense ratios, 62; "gag" clauses in, 69; indicators of excellence, 61; qualitative goals, 135–36; of national companies, 5; self-sponsorship, 101; sources of information on, 63–65; utilization measures, 62. See also community hospital health plan case study
Health Plan Employer Data and Information Set (HEDIS), 68, 206
Health systems: and management of costs, 6–7; and pricing of services, 7
Healthcare, local nature of, 241–42
Healthcare delivery value chain, 45, 46
Healthcare reform, 69
Healthcare workers, multiple perspectives, 205–8
Herzberg, Frederick, 193
Hospitals: and annual price adjustments, 26–27; horizontal hospital integration strategies, 77; and management of costs, 6–7; and pricing of services, 7; and sliding scales, 25–26; as sponsors of health plans, 82; utilization review plan, 20; and zip code incentives, 26. See also inpatients
Hygiene factors, 193

194–96; strategic focus, 190–93. *See also* subjective barriers to provider-sponsored organizations

Managed care strategy, 2; attitude toward managed care, 2–3; core products, 88–89; cost, 5; critical components of, 93; identification of plans, 10–11; image, 4; location, 3–4; physician network, 4; pricing strategy, 11; product strategy, 11; quality outcomes, 5–6; risk and nonrisk components, 89; tiered approach, 88; uniqueness of services, 5

Managed Medicaid, 234; income prerequisites, 234–35. *See also* Medicaid delivery system

Markets: fragmented payer markets, 82; mature markets, 79–80

Market dynamics, 44

Market mix, 85–86; traditional perspectives, 86

Market share, 79

Marketing, erroneous views of, 94–95n. 2

Medical costs, 68–69

Medical management, 214; challenges, 221–22; and demand management, 216–17; guidelines, 218; and performance improvement, 217–18; and provider panel management, 216–17

Medicaid delivery system, 123, 235; and access and outreach, 236; dedicated providers, 235–36; and education, 236–37; and integration, 236; preventive care, 236

Medicare, 38, 39, 66, 68, 123

Mercer, William M., 247

National Committee for Quality Assurance, 55, 135

National Demonstration Project for Quality in Healthcare, 41, 73, 107, 145, 201

National health insurance, 38

National Research Corporation, 248

Operations management, 232; key functions, 232–33; and organizational structure, 234; and operational quality, 233

Outlier provisions, 27–28

Outpatients: case rates, 33–35; and discounts off of charges, 31–32; and per-visit fees, 32–33

Pareto principle, 230

Partial risk contracting, 155; budget model, 155; capitation-based model, 156; and percent of prior years' experience, 156

Patient days, 26

Patient-day equivalents, 26

Payers, 48, 66

Payment adequacy, 125

Payment levels, 128; adjustments, 129–30; definition of covered services, 129; fee schedule assumptions, 130; incentives, 131; and payment reasonableness, 128–29; utilization assumptions, 129

Per member per month (PMPM),
104, 114, 131, 136, 137, 142
Per member per year (PMPY), 136
Percent-of-premium pricing, 30–31
Pharmacy costs, 249–50
Physician profiling, 222–23;
cautions, 224–25; two
approaches, 224
Physician–hospital organizations
(PHOS), 8, 49, 132–33, 165, 187,
195–96, 199; and carve outs,
25; factors affecting success, 76
Physicians: hospital-based, 128;
importance to payers and
hospitals, 77; and management
of costs, 7–8; physician-
physician structures, 77; and
preventive services, 8. *See also*
physician profiling; primary
care physicians
Point of service (POS), 16, 48
Preferred provider organizations
(PPOS), 11, 18, 47, 48, 53–54,
66–67, 189, 201, 222–23; and
"any willing provider" laws, 69;
insurer-sponsored, 54; market
for, 66; and networks, 18, 53–54;
weaknesses of, 58, 59
Prescription drug use, 109
Pricing: discount-from-retail,
91; on the margin, 23–24;
multiple-of-wholesale, 91;
pricing model, 91–92; options,
14–15; price determination,
16, 18; range variables, 91–92;
selection of pricing method,
15–16; strategies, 121–22. *See
also* inpatients; outpatients

Primary care physicians (PCPS), 79,
132, 139, 140, 191
Prospective Payment System, 67
Prudential, 84

Quality improvement, 109–10
Quality Improvement System for
Managed Care (QISMC), 207

RAND Corporation, 222
Resource utilization, 108–9
Retail healthcare, 253
Risk sharing, 71–72, 91, 197;
guidelines, 134
Risk structure, 113–14. *See also*
aggregated risk pool
Risk-based contracting, 104–
11, 119, 148; global, 13–14;
infrastructure, 183. *See also*
risk-based contracting, critical
elements of; risk-based
contracting, implications of
Risk-based contracting, critical
elements of, 141–42; adequate
revenue, 142; control over
service, 144–45; experienced
staff, 142; information systems,
143; medical excellence, 143;
physician leadership, 142;
specialists, 143–44; tangible
risk-reward, 144. *See also* partial
risk contracting
Risk-based contracting, implications
of, 183–84, 186–87;
and changed business
definition, 189; and extensive
collaboration, 187–88; and
longer-term contracts, 188–89;

and operational requirements, 184–86; and ownership, 187; tactical, 184

About the Authors

Robert S. Bonney, J.D., FACHE

Mr. Bonney is currently vice president for managed care and senior vice president for product lines at the Saint Luke's Shawnee Mission Health System. Prior to this position he had over 23 years of healthcare operations experience, including simultaneously serving as senior vice president of an integrated delivery system and executive vice president and chief operating officer of the system's two largest hospitals, and more recently serving as executive director of a 170,000 member managed care organization.

Mr. Bonney holds a master's degrees in both business administration (with concentrations in finance and personnel management) and health services management from the University of Missouri-Columbia and a law degree, *summa cum laude*, from the Detroit College of Law. He has co-authored a book, several book chapters, and numerous articles on the subject of managed care, and currently holds faculty appointments at the Harvard School of Public Health, the University of Missouri–Columbia, and the University of Kansas.

Mr. Bonney is board certified in healthcare management and a Fellow in the American College of Healthcare Executives (ACHE). He has been an ACHE faculty member for 17 years and developed the first series of on-line courses in managed care offered by the College.

Robert J. Smith

Robert J. Smith is vice president, strategic planning and managed care for St. Joseph's/Candler Health System in Savannah, Georgia, a regional health network serving 35 counties in southeast Georgia. His responsibilities include managed care contracting, industrial medicine, PPO management, Internet strategy development, and planning. Mr. Smith's expertise in healthcare derives from more than 20 years as CEO of a hospital-physician—sponsored HMO, a senior vice presidency in a managed care management and insurance company, and time spent as a community hospital administrator and consultant.